# OUR AMAZING CREATED
# SOLAR SYSTEM

16 articles by 8 authors document that
God created our amazing solar system

Edited by Russell Grigg

ISBN: 978-1-942773-33-7

Editor: Russell Grigg
Cover, Design & Layout: Tim Kneipp
Illustration: Caleb Salisbury

Scripture quotations are from the ESV unless otherwise indicated.
Images of spacecraft, planets, etc. are from NASA unless otherwise indicated.
The various chapters originally appeared as articles in *Creation* magazine and are
here updated. The contributing authors are from a variety of English-speaking
countries, each with its own spelling traditions; however this book conforms
to Creation Ministries International's own hybrid spelling system involving
aspects of both British spelling (e.g. "colour", not "color") and American spelling
(e.g. "realize", not "realise").

CREATION
BOOK PUBLISHERS

Atlanta, Georgia, USA
www.creationbookpublishers.com

For further information on creation/evolution
and the Christian worldview go to

**CREATION.com**

# Contents

# About the Authors

**Gary Bates** is CEO of Creation Ministries International (US) based in Atlanta, Georgia. He has been involved in the creation/evolution debate, with CMI for over 20 years, and is CMI's resident authority on the UFO/aliens phenomenon and its evolution connection. See: creation.com/bates.

**David Catchpoole, B.Ag.Sc.(Hons), Ph.D.** (University of New England) has had several articles from his research published in secular science journals. He was a plant physiologist and science educator, and then for many years a scientist/speaker for CMI (Australia). He continues to write for CMI. See creation.com/catchpoole.

**Russell Grigg, M.Sc.(Hons)** majored in Chemistry at Victoria University College, Wellington, NZ, and was an industrial chemist before serving 20 years with Overseas Missionary Fellowship (now OMF International). He has been a Staff member of CMI (Australia) for over 25 years. See: creation.com/grigg.

**Andrew Lamb, B.Sc., Dip. Ed.** majored in Computer Science at the University of Queensland, and gained his Diploma of Education from the Queensland University of Technology. He has been a staff member of CMI since 2000, serving in various capacities. See: creation.com/andrew-lamb.

**Spike Psarris, B.Sc.** majored in Electrical Engineering at the University of Massachusetts and has done graduate work in Physics. He was formerly an engineer in the United States military space program, which he entered as an atheist evolutionist, but left it as a young-earth creationist Christian. See: creation.com/psarris

**Jonathan Sarfati, B.Sc.(Hons), Ph.D., F.M.** Dr Sarfati's Ph.D. is from Victoria University, Wellington, NZ. He is the author of some of the world's best-known creation books. A former NZ Chess Champion, he worked for CMI in Australia 1996–2010, and since then in Atlanta, USA. See: creation.com/sarfati.

**Wayne Spencer, M.S., B.S.** obtained his master's degree in Physics from Wichita State University in Kansas, USA. Active in creationist circles, he has taught Science and Math, and now works in computer technical support in Dallas, Texas, USA. See: creation.com/wayne-spencer.

**Tas Walker, B.Sc.(Hons), B.Eng.(Hons), Ph.D.** worked in power station design and operation and the geological assessment of coal deposits. He developed a geological model to connect geology to biblical history, and now works full-time researching and speaking for CMI Australia. See: creation.com/tas-walker.

# Foreword

How awe inspiring is the sight of the heavens on a dark night away from city lights! Of all the heavenly objects on display, those belonging to our own solar system are the brightest in the sky, from the moon, which dominates when visible, to the brilliance of Venus, Mars, Jupiter and Saturn. Turn even a modest telescope to the moon and the planets and you will be treated to a fascinating variety from the phases of Venus, the redness of Mars, the clearly visible Galilean moons orbiting Jupiter, and the stunning rings surrounding Saturn.

The more we learn about the system of planets, comets and asteroids that orbit our sun, the more it becomes evident, for those who will see, that there is a profound intellect behind the design of the solar system. The secularists have tried in vain to account for the existence of the solar system in naturalistic terms, but the observations stubbornly refuse to comply with such attempts.

This book provides compelling evidence confirming the Bible's account of God's creative activity on Day 4 of Creation Week which is an eye-witness account of what actually happened when the sun, moon, and stars were created.

A prolific author in his own right, with many articles in *Creation* magazine over the years, Russell Grigg has turned his hand to editing this collection of articles from past issues of *Creation* and has brought them up to date with our rapidly expanding knowledge of the solar system.

You will be truly enriched by reading this book with its brilliant illustrations and lay-level explanations of the observations that experimental science has made. The evidence is overwhelming that the solar system has been created. As Sir Isaac Newton, perhaps the greatest scientist to have ever lived, observed: "This most beautiful system of the sun, planets, and comets could only proceed from the counsel and dominion of an intelligent Being".

Be inspired as you read and give God the glory!

*Mark Harwood, B.Sc., B.,E., Ph.D.: scientist, speaker, and writer for Creation Ministries International*

**Dr Harwood is a former satellite scientist whose graduate studies were focused on radio-telescopes and computer techniques for antenna design and measurement. His background includes the design of satellites for the communications industry, where he played a key role in the development of Australia's national satellite system.**

# Introduction

## What is the solar system?

Our solar system consists principally of the star we call the sun; the four inner terrestrial (or rocky) planets Mercury, Venus, Earth, and Mars; the four outer giant gaseous planets Jupiter, Saturn, Uranus and Neptune; and many dwarf planets (as currently categorized) of which five are officially recognized: Pluto, Ceres, Haumea, Makemake, and Eris. The solar system also contains the moons of all these planets, plus numerous Trans-Neptunian objects (TNOs) that are sometimes called Kuiper Belt objects (KBOs), plus comets, asteroids, meteors and smaller bodies, all of which orbit the sun; plus dust, cosmic rays, and the solar wind.

Some writers define the solar system's edge as being the point where the solar wind finally stops. The space probe *Voyager 1*, launched in 1977, may have finally reached this point at 18.2 billion km (11.3 billion miles) from the sun (*Nature* **489**(7414) News; 5 Sept. 2012). If so, this is the first man-made object to leave the solar system.

## Where did the solar system come from?

Either it formed all by itself as per the nebular hypothesis, as evolutionists claim, or it was created by God, as the Bible says. In this book we will tour the solar system and consider the evidence. Our purpose is two-fold: first, to provide accurate information about our solar system; second, to demonstrate how the record in Genesis of creation by God fits the data best.

Many of the planets and moons in the solar system appear to be young, and they also show evidence of design by an intelligent Creator. One chapter deals with the perennial question: "Did life come to Earth from outer space?"; another: "Did God create life on other planets?". These chapters detail the enormous problems involved in these ideas for evolutionists.

Facts and figures for the planets, supplied in each chapter, as well as being tabled in the Appendix, are based on the latest data supplied by NASA space probes, when this book was published.

# Chapter 1

# Solar system origin: Nebular hypothesis

According to the eyewitness account in Genesis, God created the earth on Day 1 of Creation Week, and the sun and moon on Day 4, most likely along with the planets. However, evolutionists reject a Creator *a priori*, so they need to come up with another explanation. The leading candidate is called the *nebular hypothesis*. This proposes that the sun, the earth and the rest of the solar system formed from a *nebula,* or cloud of dust and gas that supposedly contracted or collapsed due to its own gravity.

**Author: Jonathan Sarfati**[1]

| | Mercury | Venus | Earth | Mars | Jupiter |
|---|---|---|---|---|---|
| Day (in hours) | 4,222.6 | 2,802 | 24 | 24.7 | 9.9 |
| Year (in days) | 88 | 224.7 | 365.2 | 687 | 4,331 |
| Mean Temp. | 167°C | 464°C | 15°C | -65°C | -110°C |

## Evolutionary problems

The best known pioneer of this was French atheistic mathematician Pierre-Simon Laplace (1749–1827).[2] The nebular hypothesis is now the most widely accepted model used to explain the formation of our solar system by the process of evolution. It was originally applied to our solar system only, but is now applied to the rest of the universe also.[3] Nevertheless, despite the dogmatic support given to this theory by evolutionary astronomers, it has a number of huge problems.

## Origin of stars

First of all, if the collapsing cloud theory can't even explain the sun alone, then it is doomed from the start. To form the sun, or any star, a cloud must be dense enough to collapse and compress the interior so that it becomes hot enough for nuclear fusion to start. But in a typical nebula, the outward gas pressure is far greater than the inward gravitation.

The British mathematician and astrophysicist James Jeans (1877–1946) calculated how massive a cloud must be so that gravity can overcome the tendency for gas to expand. The main points are: high density favours collapse, and high temperature favours expansion. The minimum mass he calculated relates to both of these, and is now called the *Jeans Mass* ($M_J$).[4]

But according to the big bang theory, at the time the first stars were formed, the temperature was so high that the required Jeans Mass would be about 100,000 suns.[5] This is about the same mass as a globular cluster, i.e. no cloud less massive than this could have collapsed into a star, thus no star could have formed this way.[6]

All theories of star formation have problems.[7] Some include a shockwave from an exploding star, but this doesn't explain where *that* star came from. Ph.D. astrophysicist Jason Lisle points out another problem:

"Even if we could compress the nebula sufficiently to the point that the force of gravity was strong enough to prevent the gas from expanding, other effects would kick in, thereby preventing the formation of a star. Clouds of gas always have a weak magnetic field, which would be concentrated if the cloud were compressed. This dramatically increases the field strength. The magnetic pressure would halt a shrinking cloud and drive it to re-expand. It's a bit like trying to push the like poles of two magnets together."[8]

Neil deGrasse Tyson, evolutionary astrophysicist and fanatical atheist, admits:

"Not all gas clouds in the Milky Way can form stars at

| Saturn | Uranus | Neptune | Pluto |
|---|---|---|---|
| 10.7 | 17.2 | 16.1 | 153.5 |
| 10,747 | 30,589 | 59,800 | 90,560 |
| -140°C | -195°C | -200°C | -225°C |

all times. More often than not, the cloud is confused about what to do next. Actually, astrophysicists are the confused ones here. We know the cloud wants to collapse under its own weight to make one or more stars. But rotation as well as turbulent motion within the cloud work against that fate. So, too, does the ordinary gas pressure you learned about in high-school chemistry class. Galactic magnetic fields also fight collapse: they penetrate the cloud and latch onto any free-roaming charged particles contained therein, restricting the ways in which the cloud will respond to its self-gravity. The scary part is that if none of us knew in advance that stars exist, front line research would offer plenty of convincing reasons for why stars could never form."[9]

## Origin of planets

So, stars alone can't be explained by such naturalistic conjectures. However, the planets pose even more difficulties for evolutionists to explain, with several additional problems, as outlined below.

## Angular momentum

One major problem can be shown by accomplished skaters spinning on ice. As skaters pull their arms in, they spin faster. This effect is due to what physicists call the *Law of Conservation of Angular Momentum*. Angular momentum = mass × velocity × distance from the centre of mass, and always stays constant in an isolated system. When the skaters pull their arms in, the distance from the centre decreases, so they spin faster or else angular momentum would not stay constant.

In the formation of our sun from a nebula in space, the same effect would have occurred as the gases allegedly contracted into the centre to form the sun. This would have caused the sun to spin very rapidly. But our sun spins very slowly, while the planets move very rapidly around the sun. In fact, although the sun has over 99% of the mass of the solar system, it has only 2% of the angular momentum. This pattern is directly *opposite* to the pattern predicted for the nebular hypothesis.

Evolutionists have tried hard to solve this problem. In a leading textbook, well-known solar system scientist Dr Stuart Ross Taylor notes "angular momentum must be transferred outwards … and a wide variety of physical processes have been suggested". He then gives details of some current favourites, including 'gravitational torque' in an asymmetrical disk,[10] before admitting "a predictive theory of nebular evolution is still lacking".[11]

## Sun's axial tilt

If the sun and the planets were formed by a collapsing nebula, then the sun should be spinning in the same plane as the planets. However, its axis is tilted 7.25°

away from the ecliptic, which is defined by Earth's orbit. A better comparison would be Jupiter's orbital plane, since it has most of the planetary mass and angular momentum of the solar system. Jupiter's orbital inclination is 1.308° from the ecliptic, so this still leaves almost 6° difference. The anomalous tilts of the planets are usually explained by invoking collisions, but this would not apply to the sun.

## Rocky planets

Evolutionary astronomers believe that the planets arose from collisions of dust particles which heated and stuck together to form larger accretions of welded rock. These blobs further accreted to form larger and larger blobs, at a certain stage melting into spheres, and thus the inner planets were formed: Mercury, Venus, Earth and Mars. However, research has shown that the rocks would not stick, but most likely "simply zoom past each other or collide and recoil like snooker balls."[12]

## Gas giants

According to evolutionary models, the huge planets Jupiter and Saturn could have formed only if they were far enough away from the sun so that ice could

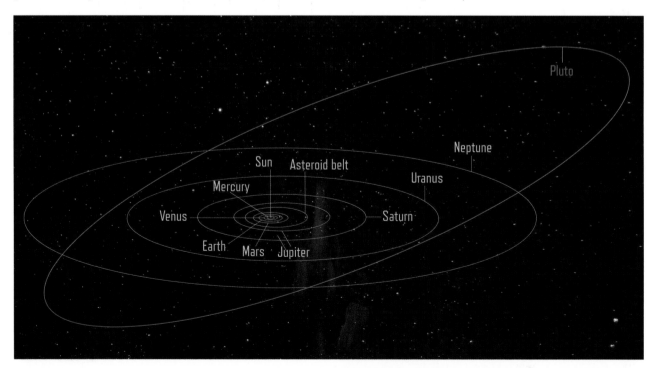

**The plane of the earth's orbit around the sun is called the plane of the ecliptic (or just the ecliptic). The sun's apparent path through the sky lies in this plane. The other seven planets orbit the sun in nearly same plane. However, Pluto orbits the sun with an inclination to the ecliptic of 17°.**

condense. This would provide additional mass to draw in gas from the nebula, and the ice would help the rocks to bond. Jupiter's core would need to be about 20 Earth masses to do this, but models of Jupiter indicate that its core is actually only about 5 Earth masses at the most, if it even exists.[13]

And simulations indicate that the solar nebula would have dissipated before the core had a chance to grow big enough. Furthermore, the friction of the gas and dust in the nebular disk would slow the planets' orbits so they would spiral into the sun. When it comes to the 'Ice Giants', Uranus and Neptune (Chapters 12 and 13), the problems are even more acute, as one evolutionary astronomer admitted:

> "Pssst ... astronomers who model the formation of the solar system have kept a dirty little secret: Uranus and Neptune don't exist. Or at least computer simulations have never explained how planets as big as the two gas giants could form so far from the sun. Bodies orbited so slowly in the outer parts of the solar system that the slow process of gravitational accretion would need more time than the age of the solar system to form bodies with 14.5 and 17.1 times the mass of Earth."[14]

To solve the problem of insufficient matter in the outer reaches of the solar system, some evolutionists have proposed that the gas giants formed closer to the sun and migrated outwards. For example, to form Uranus and Neptune, the model requires limiting the disk of nebular material to only 30 Astronomical Units in diameter. This makes it difficult for this model to account for the many even more distant objects in the solar system, such as Pluto (39 AU).

Furthermore, giant planets around other stars also confound the nebular hypothesis (see Chapter 16). Here, the problem is that they are too close to their star so that ice would never have condensed, as per the standard model. So evolutionists have proposed that they formed further out and migrated inwards. But then the problem is halting this migration so they don't fall into their star in a 'death spiral'.[15]

It's common for evolutionists to pile on *ad hoc* hypotheses to try to salvage their evolutionary model. The evolutionist's nebular hypothesis is no exception to this, as shown.

## Retrograde motion

The nebular hypothesis predicts that as the nebula spiralled inwards, all the resulting planets and comets would rotate and orbit in the same direction (*prograde*). But Venus rotates in the opposite direction, called *retrograde* (see also Chapter 4). Furthermore, a comet and several exoplanets have been discovered with retrograde *orbits* (see Chapter 15 Feature, and Chapter 16).

## Conclusion

Although the nebular hypothesis is accepted uncritically by many evolutionists, there are severe problems with forming both the sun and the planets from a collapsing cloud. The best explanation is still, "By the word of the Lord the heavens were made, and by the breath of his mouth all their host" (Psalm 33:6).

## References and Notes

1. This chapter adapted and updated from Sarfati, J., *Creation* **32**(3):34–35, 2010; creation.com/nebular-hypothesis.
2. Laplace, P., *Exposition du Système du Monde* (*Exposition of the System of the* World), 1796.
3. The modern variant that is most accepted is the Solar Nebular Disk Model (SNDM)." universetoday.com.
4. Jeans Mass ($M_J$) = $K \rho^{-\frac{1}{2}} T^{3/2}$, where K is a constant, $\rho$ is the density, and T is the temperature. Alternatively, this can be expressed as $M_J \approx 45 M_\odot\, n^{-\frac{1}{2}} T^{3/2}$, where $M_\odot$ is the solar mass, n is the density of atoms per $cm^3$, and T is the temperature in Kelvins.
5. According to big bang theory, the temperature was about 3,000 and density about 6,000, therefore $M_J \approx 10^5 M_\odot$.
6. Wiebe, D.Z. *et al.*, Problems of star formation theory and prospects of submillimeter observations, Cornell University Library, arxiv.org, 21 July 2008.
7. Hartmann, L., *Accretion Processes in Star Formation*, 2nd edition, pp. 57–58, Cambridge University Press, 2008.
8. Lisle, J., Blue stars confirm recent creation, *Acts & Facts* **41**(9):16, 2012; icr.org/ article/6943.
9. Tyson, N. deG., *Death by Black Hole and Other Cosmic Quandaries*, p. 187, W. W. Norton & Company, 2007.
10. Taylor, S., *Solar System Evolution: A New Perspective*, 2nd ed., pp. 63-64, Cambridge University Press, 2001.
11. Ref. 10, p. 64, citing Cassen, P., in *Paul Pellas Symposium*, MNHN Paris, p.39, 1998.
12. Muir, H., Earth was a freak, *New Scientist* **177**(2388):24, 29 March 2003; see also Chapter 5.
13. Planetary evolutionary core theory collapses, *Creation* **27**(1):7, 2004, after *New Scientist* **183**(2457):9, 24 July 2004, where noted planetary theorist Alan Boss admits, "The leading theory for giant planet formation has encountered a mortal blow."
14. Naeye, R., Birth of Uranus and Neptune, *Astronomy* **28**(4):30, 2000.
15. Than, K., Death spiral: why theorists can't make solar systems, space.com, 15 January 2007. See also Spencer, W., Planets and migrating theories, creation.com/migratingplanets, 13 February 2007.

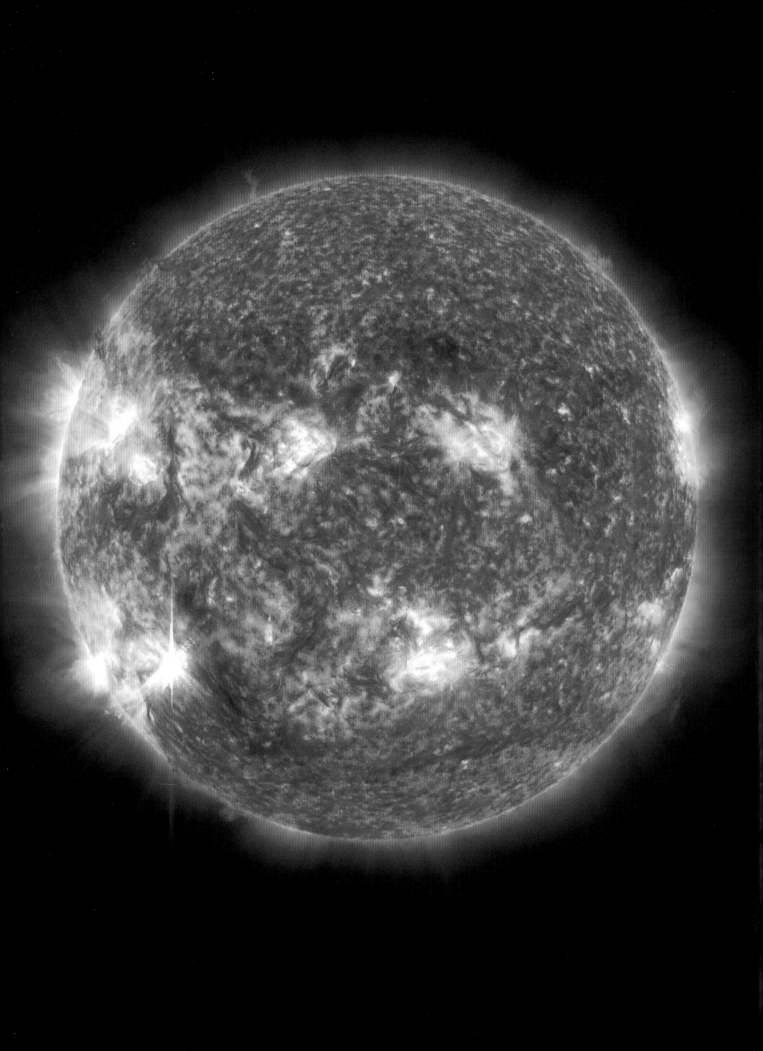

# Chapter 2

# The Sun: our special star

The sun—this hot, bright ball of plasma—dominates the daytime sky, and is by far the most massive object in our solar system. Over 1 million Earths would fit inside the sun. It is exactly the right distance from Earth to provide the heat and light that our trees and plants need. It also evaporates water from our oceans, lakes, and rivers to form the clouds that provide the rain that sustains our crops and gives us fresh water to drink. For us, it is certainly no ordinary star.

**Author: Jonathan Sarfati**[1]

## The sun's origin

According to God's Word, the Bible, the sun did not always light the earth. God didn't make it until Day 4 of Creation Week, while the earth was created on Day 1. This refutes ideas like 'God used evolution' and 'God created over billions of years', because they all assert that the sun arose before the earth.[2] For the first three days of its existence, the earth was lit by the light which God created on Day 1 (Genesis 1:3),[3] while the day/night cycle was caused by the earth's rotation relative to this directional light source. Then according to Genesis 1:14–19.

> "And God said, 'Let there be lights in the expanse of the heavens to separate the day from the night. And let them be for signs and for seasons, and for days and years, and let them be lights in the expanse of the heavens to give light upon the earth.' And it was so. And God made the two great lights—the greater light to rule the day and the lesser light to rule the night—and the stars. And God set them in the expanse of the heavens to give light upon the earth, to rule over the day and over the night; and to separate the light from the darkness. And God saw that it was good. And there was evening and there was morning, the fourth day."

In the New Jerusalem of Revelation 21:23, there will also be no need for the sun, because God will provide the light once again. But meanwhile, we can appreciate the wonder of the star God has provided for us.

An artistic impression of the NASA Solar Dynamics Observatory in orbit around the earth. The purpose is to study violent sun activity that can disrupt communications, knock out power stations, and disable satellites on the earth.

## How is the sun special?

Anti-theists are fond of dismissing the sun as a run-of-the-mill star in a not-too-special place in a spiral arm of the Milky Way Galaxy. It is true that many stars are far bigger and brighter than the sun. However, saying that bigger stars are more important is as illogical as saying that a 7-foot man is more important than a 5-foot woman.

Recent research has called the sun 'exceptional'.[4] Our sun is among the top 10% (by mass) of stars in its neighbourhood (most stars are red dwarfs invisible to the naked eye). It is actually an ideal size to support life on Earth. There would be little point in having a red supergiant star like Betelgeuse, because it is so huge that it would engulf all the inner planets![5] Nor would we want a star like the blue-white supergiant Rigel, about 120,000 times as bright as the sun, and emitting too much high-frequency radiation.[6] Conversely, a star much smaller than our sun would be too faint to support life, unless the planet was so close to the star that there would be dangerous gravitational tides.

The sun is in an ideal environment. It is a single star—most stars exist in multiple-star systems. A planet in such a system would suffer extreme temperature variations. The sun's position in our spiral Milky Way Galaxy is also ideal. Its orbit (within this galaxy) is fairly circular, meaning that it won't go too near the inner galaxy where supernovae, extremely energetic star explosions, are more common. It also orbits almost parallel to the plane of our galaxy—otherwise, crossing this plane would be very disruptive. Furthermore, the sun is at an ideal distance from the centre of our galaxy, called the *co-rotation radius*. Only here does a star's orbital speed match that of the spiral arms—otherwise the sun could cross an arm and be exposed to supernovae.[4]

Our sun is a powerful object, often throwing out flares, and every few years (usually around sunspot maximum—see below Sunspots, Galileo and heliocentrism) more violent eruptions called coronal mass ejections. These cause huge electric currents in Earth's upper atmosphere and disrupt power grids and satellites. In 1989, one disabled a power grid in northern Quebec. Nevertheless the sun is an 'exceptionally stable'[7] star. Three astronomers recently

The sun and everything that orbits it make up the solar system, including the eight planets, and five named dwarf planets. Distances are not to scale; Asteroid and Keiper Belts are mostly empty space.

studied single stars of the same size, brightness and composition as the sun. Almost all of them erupt about once a century in *superflares* 100 to 100 million times more powerful than the one that blacked out Quebec. If the sun were to erupt in such a superflare, it would destroy Earth's ozone layer, with catastrophic results for life.[8]

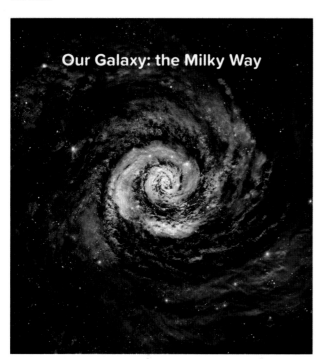

Our Galaxy: the Milky Way

## How does the sun shine?

In 1939, Hans Bethe proposed that the sun and other stars are powered by *nuclear fusion*—this theory earned him the 1967 Nobel Prize for Physics.[9] In fusion, extremely fast-moving hydrogen nuclei join to form helium—this requires temperatures of millions of degrees. Some mass is lost and converted into a huge amount of energy as per Einstein's famous formula $E = mc^2$.[10] Thus the sun is like a gigantic hydrogen bomb.[11] Four million tonnes of matter are converted into energy every second—this is huge, but negligible compared to the sun's enormous total mass of $1.99 \times 10^{30}$ (1,990,000,000,000,000,000,000,000,000,000) kg.

Fusion in stars generally combines four hydrogen nuclei into one helium nucleus.[12] This actually provides an upper limit to the sun's age (see below Our steady sun: a problem for billions of years). Fusion also produces a vast number of extremely low-mass particles called neutrinos that travel almost as fast as light.[13] These ghostly particles can pass untouched through matter light-years in thickness. They are now known to switch between 'flavours' (types).[14]

"Concerning the alleged long age of the sun, a leading solar astronomer once commented: 'I suspect … that the Sun is 4.5 billion years old. However, given some new and unexpected results to the contrary,

**Earth is dwarfed here in approximate relative size to the sun. The length of this eruption extends about 250,000 km out from the sun. Earth is about 12,750 km in diameter, so the eruption is about 20 times the diameter of our planet.**

and some time for some frantic recalculations and theoretical readjustment, I suspect that we could live with Bishop Ussher's value for the age of the Earth and Sun [about 6,000 years]. I don't think there is much in the way of observational evidence to conflict with that.'"[15]

## Our steady sun: a problem for billions of years

All living things on the earth ultimately obtain their energy from the sun, as do the wind and water cycles. And nuclear fusion reactions power the sun. In theory, as four hydrogen nuclei fuse to form one helium nucleus, they would take less room and the sun's core should shrink. This would make further fusion reactions occur more readily. Therefore, the sun should shine more brightly as it ages.

But this means that if billions of years were true, the sun would have been much fainter in the past. However, there is no evidence that the sun was fainter at any time in the earth's history. Astronomers call

this the 'faint young sun paradox', but it is no paradox at all if the sun is only as old as the Bible says—about 6,000 years.

Evolutionists and long-agers believe that life appeared on the earth about 3.8 billion years ago. But if that timescale were true, the sun would be 25% brighter today than it was back then. This implies that back then (with a cooler sun) the earth would have been frozen at an average temperature of –3° C. However, most palaeontologists believe that, if anything, the earth was warmer in the past.[16] The only way around this is for them to make arbitrary and unrealistic assumptions of a far greater greenhouse effect at that time than exists today,[17] with about 1,000 times more $CO_2$ in the atmosphere than there is today.[18]

However, the scientific evidence is consistent with the sun having the age that we would expect from reading of the Bible. In 6,000 years or so, there would have been no significant increase in energy output from the sun. It is a problem only for old-age ideas.

## Sunspots, Galileo and heliocentrism

Sunspots (*below*) look like dark patches on the sun. They can be seen to move, and analyzing them shows that different parts of the sun rotate at different rates, unlike a solid body. Sunspots come and go in cycles of about 11.2 years. Galileo Galilei (1564–1642) systematically studied sunspots in 1611 and realized that they upset the prevailing Aristotelian/Ptolemaic view that the heavenly bodies were 'perfect spheres'.[19]

Today we realize that sunspots are vortices of gas on the sun's surface, and appear dark because they are several thousand degrees cooler than the rest of the sun. Analysis of their light spectra shows that the sun's magnetic field is especially strong in sunspots.[20]

Galileo supported the theory of Nicolaus Copernicus (1473–1543) that the earth and other planets move around the sun. Anti-Christian propagandists make much of the conflict between Galileo and the Church, or 'science vs religion'. But Galileo thought that the much simpler mathematics of the Copernican system compared to the unwieldy Ptolemaic system would best reflect God's mathematical simplicity (i.e. God is not composed of parts but is Triune). The *Encyclopædia Britannica* identifies Galileo's main opponents as the scientific establishment:

> "The Aristotelian professors, seeing their vested interests threatened, united against him. They strove to cast suspicion on him in the eyes of the ecclesiastical authorities because of [alleged] contradictions between the Copernican theory and Scriptures."[21]

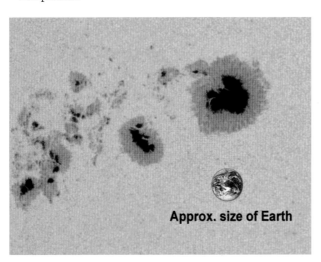

**Approx. size of Earth**

**Sunspots (shown) can be as large as the earth.**

**Galileo struggled against the anti-biblical 'science' of his day.**

Giorgio de Santillana (1902–1974), Professor of the History of Science at Massachusetts Institute of Technology, pointed out that contrary to myth:

> "It has been known for a long time that a major part of the church's intellectuals were on the side of Galileo, while the clearest opposition to him came from secular ideas."[22]

Both sides should have realized that all movement must be described *in relation to something else*—a *reference frame*—and from a descriptive point of view, *all reference frames are equally valid*. The Bible writers used the *earth* as a convenient reference frame, as do modern astronomers talking about 'sunset'; speed limit signs also depend on the earth as a reference frame. Using the sun (or the centre of mass of the solar system) is the most convenient for discussing planetary motions.[23,24]

## Eclipse!

A *solar eclipse* occurs when the moon passes between the sun and the earth so that the sun is totally or partially obscured. This happens during a new moon, when the sun and moon are in conjunction as seen from the earth. A total solar eclipse is a spectacular phenomenon, but **should never be viewed without special equipment to prevent eye damage**. This awesome sight will occur in different parts of the world in 2016, 2017, 2019, and 2020.

For a few seconds near the beginning and again at the end of a total solar eclipse the sun shines through valleys in the moon's mountainous surface causing beads of light to be seen; they are named after English astronomer Francis Baily (1774–1884) who first deduced what caused them. When just one Baily's bead is left or appears, it and the corona look like a diamond ring. This artist's impression combines these effects.

A total eclipse is possible because the moon is almost exactly the same angular size (half a degree) in the sky as the sun—it is both 400 times smaller and 400 times closer than the sun. This looks very much like design. The moon is gradually receding from the earth at 4 cm (1½ inches) per year. If this had really been going on for billions of years, and mankind had been around for a tiny fraction of that time, the chance of mankind living at a time so they could observe this precise size matchup would be remote. (Actually, this recession puts an upper limit on the age of the earth/moon system at far less than the assumed 4.5 billion years—see Chapter 8).

Creationist astronomer Prof. Danny Faulkner[25] has shown that solar eclipses (as seen from the earth) are unique in the solar system—no other planet/moon combination comes close.[26]

During a total eclipse, the sun's outer atmosphere, the *corona*, is visible. This comprises extremely thin ionised gas, which is extremely hot. At 2 million °C, it is about 350 times hotter than the sun's surface. This has been a mystery, because heat normally flows from hot objects to cooler ones. One promising

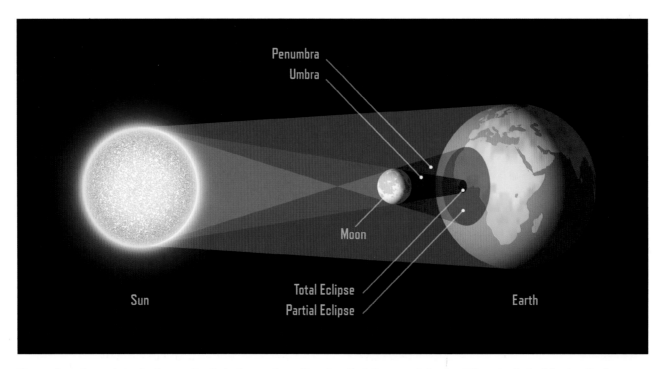

Penumbra
Umbra
Moon
Total Eclipse
Partial Eclipse
Sun
Earth

The region of complete shadow on Earth during a solar eclipse is called the moon's 'umbra' (from Latin for 'shadow'); observers within this area see a total eclipse of the sun. The region of partial shadow is called the penumbra (from Latin *paene* for 'almost' or 'nearly'); observers here see a partial eclipse. The earth's surface outside the penumbra is fully lit by the sun, so no eclipse is seen here.

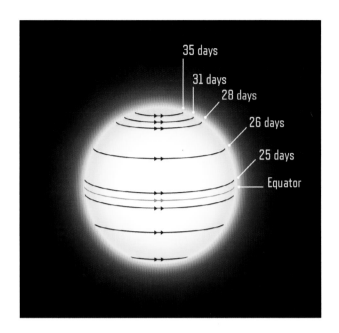

theory (which still needs work) involves the sun's strong magnetic field—reconnection of magnetic flux lines could release large amounts of energy into the corona.[27,28] This could have applications in fusion power research. Another theory involves magnetic fields 'whipping' coronal gas back and forth.[29] However as one textbook notes, "the heating of the solar corona … is still one of the unsolved mysteries in natural science."[30]

## What colour is the sun?

If you ask people this question, most will say 'yellow'. But this is not correct. If you shine yellow light on a white surface or through mist, it will appear yellow. Yet during the daylight, white objects looks white, and fluffy clouds in a blue sky look white as well. This means that white light must be shining on them.

Thus, in reality, the sun is *white*. However, the sun is actually all colours mixed together, which we see as white, but which we can also see separated in a rainbow. The colours in a rainbow from outer (longest

**Because the sun is made of plasma (ionized gas), it is fluid and so is able to rotate faster at its equator than at its poles. The sun's equator takes about 25 days and the poles about 35 days to make one full sidereal rotation (i.e. in relation to the other stars), so the sun is continually slowly changing shape.**

# Sun Facts

| | |
|---|---|
| Mean distance from Earth | 150 million km or 93 million miles, More precisely 149,597,871,700 metres = 1 Astronomical Unit (AU) (= 8.317 light minutes, = 499 light seconds) As defined by the International Astronomical Union in 2012 |
| Mean radius | 695,700 km or 432,290 miles (109 × Earth) |
| Mass | 1,988,500 × $10^{24}$ kg (333,000 × Earth) |
| Volume | 1,412,000 × $10^{12}$ km³ (1,304,000 × Earth) |
| Mean density | 1408 kg/m³ (25.5% Earth) |
| Surface gravity | 274 m/s² (28 × Earth) |
| Escape velocity | 617.6 km/s or 383.76 miles/sec (55.2 × Earth) |
| Sidereal rotation period | ~25 Earth days at equator; ~35 Earth days at poles |
| Power output (luminosity) | 382.8 × $10^{24}$ J/s |
| Mass conversion rate | 4260 million kg/s |
| Temperature | ~15 million °C core; ~5,500° C surface; ~2,000,000° C corona |
| Photosphere composition | $H_2$ 90.965%, He 8.889%, traces C, Ne, N, Fe, Mg, Si, S |

Source: Sun Fact Sheet, NASA, updated 29 February 2016.

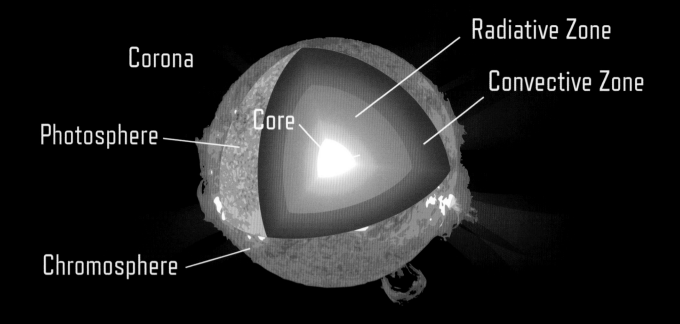

Corona

Radiative Zone

Convective Zone

Photosphere

Core

Chromosphere

# Anatomy of the Sun

400    500    600    700

**Visible light spectrum; the wavelength is in nanometres (i.e. billionths of a metre).**

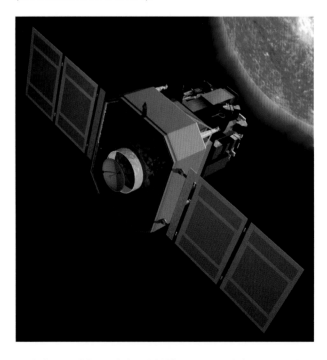

**Artistic rendition of the SOHO spacecraft in space. The telescope is facing the sun; the panels acquire energy from the sun; the small dish antenna at the rear sends data gathered back to Earth.**

wavelength) to inner (shortest wavelength) are red, orange, yellow, green, blue, indigo, violet. When the sun is low in the sky, at sunrise or sunset, it may appear red, orange or yellow, because its other (shorter wavelength) colours are scattered by the earth's atmosphere and only the red, orange or yellow get through the atmosphere for us to see.

So why are most of the images of the sun in this book red? This is an artefact of the imaging p[rocess. Most have been taken by extreme ultraviolet (EUV) imaging telescopes aboard spacecraft such as the Solar and Heliospheric Observatory (SOHO) of NASA and the European Space Agency. The EUV images come from the sun's chromosphere, which is a layer of the sun sandwiched between the sun's visible surface called the photosphere, and its atmosphere called the corona. Since UV light is invisible we need a false colour to see the features.

In the chromosphere, the temperature rises from 6000° C to about 30,000° C. At this higher temperature, hydrogen emits light that gives off a deep-red colour (called H-alpha emission). This is what gives the chromosphere its name (colour-sphere). When the Sun is viewed through EUV filters that isolate the H-alpha emission, a wealth of new features can be seen, such as flares and coronal mass ejections.

Lighter regions in these images correspond to the hottest or most energetic parts of the chromosphere.

## References and Notes

1. This chapter adapted and updated from Sarfati, J., *Creation* **22**(1): 27-31, 1999; creation.com/sun.

2. Many Christians who compromise with billions of years assert that the sun and other heavenly bodies were not really 'made' on the fourth 'day' (millions of years long). Rather, they 'appeared' to a hypothetical observer on Earth when a dense cloud layer dissipated after millions of years. But this (mis)interpretation is not allowed by the Hebrew words used. The word *'asah* means 'make' throughout Genesis 1, and is sometimes used interchangeably with 'create' (*bara'*), e.g. in Genesis 1:26-27. It is pure desperation to apply a different meaning to the same word in the same grammatical construction in the same passage, just to fit in with atheistic evolutionary ideas like the big bang. If God had *meant* 'appeared', then He presumably would have *used* the Hebrew word for appear (*ra'ah*), as when the dry land 'appeared' as the waters gathered in one place on Day 3 (Genesis 1:9). This is supported by Hebrew scholars who have translated the Bible into English. Over 20 major translations were checked, and all clearly teach that the sun, moon and stars were *made* on the fourth day.

3. See Grigg, R., Light, life and the glory of God, *Creation* **24**(1):38-39, December 2001; creation.com/light and the related article "What does 'God is light' mean?" creation.com/bible-contradiction-claims#light, 2 June 2012.

4. Chown, M., What a star! *New Scientist* **162**(2192):17, 26 June 1999.

5. Or the variable star VY Canis Majoris (VY CMa), a red hypergiant about 1,400 times the radius of the sun, large enough to engulf not just the inner planets, but even Jupiter.

6. And certainly not the brightest known star R136a1, a Wolf-Rayet star (blue and unstable), 265 times more massive and 8.7 million times brighter than the sun.

7. Seife, C., Thank our lucky star, *New Scientist* **161**(2168):15, 9 January 1999.

8. The researchers later theorized that such flares are triggered by the large magnetic field of a closely orbiting gas giant planet (reported in: Death flares, *Discover* **20**(4):19, April 1999). But the standard evolutionary accretion model forbids gas giants from forming that close to the star: they can grow large enough to attract gas only if they are cool enough to incorporate ice into the accreting body.

9. Bethe, Hans Albrecht, *The New Encyclopædia Britannica* **2**:173, 15th Ed. 1992.

10. Four hydrogen atoms (mass = 1.008) convert to helium (mass 4.0039) losing 0.0281 atomic mass units (1 AMU = 1.66 x 10$^{-27}$ kg), releasing 4.2 x 10$^{-12}$ joules of energy.

11. Man-made hydrogen bombs use the heavy hydrogen isotopes deuterium and tritium, plus some lithium. The sun uses ordinary hydrogen, which is much harder to fuse, but Bethe calculated that carbon-12 nuclei in the sun could catalyze the reaction.

12. The net fusion reaction is 4 $^1$H → $^4$He + 2e$^+$ + 2⬚e where e$^+$ is a positron or anti-electron, and ⬚e is an electron-neutrino. If the sun were powered by nuclear fission (instead of fusion) or by radioactive decay of heavy elements, *antineutrinos* would be produced instead.

13. In 2011, researchers at CERN (Switzerland) claimed that neutrinos exceeded the speed of light, but this claim has largely been discounted. See Sarfati, J., Neutrinos faster than light? Will relativity need revising? creation.com/neutrino, 11 October 2011.

14. Before this neutrino oscillation was demonstrated, this was a huge problem for the fusion theory and thus for billions of years. Theoretical physicists taught that neutrinos had precisely zero rest-mass, which would make oscillation impossible. However, in 2001, oscillation was detected, so the theorists were proven wrong. See Newton, R. (pen name at the time for astrophysicist Dr Jason Lisle of ICR.org), 'Missing' neutrinos found! No longer an 'age' indicator, *J. Creation* **16**(3):123-125, 2002; creation.com/neutrinos.

15. Eddy, J.A., quoted by Kazmann, R.G., It's about time: 4.5 billion years, *Geotimes* **23**:18-20, 1978.

16. Faulkner, D., The young faint sun paradox and the age of the solar system, *J. Creation* **15**(2):3-4, 2001; creation.com/faintsun.

17. As leading day-age defender Hugh Ross does in: The faint Sun paradox, *Facts for Faith* **10**, 2002.

18. However, analyses of acritarchs (eukaryotic algal microfossils) 'dated' to 1.4 billion years ago, when the sun would have been only 88% as bright as it is today, provide evidence for only 10-200 times today's level of CO$_2$. Still, the researchers continue to hope that this would have compensated for the fainter sun. Kaufman, A. and Xiao, S., High CO$_2$ levels in the Proterozoic atmosphere estimated from analyses of individual microfossils, *Nature* **425**(6955):279-282, 18 September 2003; comment by Mojzsis, S.J., Probing early atmospheres, same issue, pp. 249-251. See also Samec, R., The sun in time, *J. Creation* **18**(3):8-9, 2004.

19. Galileo, *Encyclopædia Britannica* **19**:638-640, 15th Ed., 1992.

20. Magnetic fields often split spectral lines—the Zeeman Effect—and this is detectable in sunspots.

21. Ref. 19, p. 638. See also Carter, R. and Safarti, J., Why the Universe does not revolve around the Earth: Refuting absolute geocentrism, creation.com/geocent, 12 February 2015.

22. de Santillana, G.D. *The Crime of Galileo* p. xii, University of Chicago Press, Chicago, 1955.

23. Grigg, R., The Galileo 'twist' *Creation* **19**(4):30-32, 1997; creation.com/gal-twist.

24. Sarfati, J., *Refuting Evolution*, ch. 7, 5th ed., Creation Book Publishers, 2012.

25. See He made the stars also ..., *Interview with creationist astronomer Danny Faulkner, Creation* **19**(4):18-21, 1997; creation.com/stars-also.

26. Faulkner, D., The angular size of the Moon and other planetary satellites: an argument for design, *Creation Research Society Quarterly* **35**(1):23-26, June 1998; creationresearch.org/crsq/articles/35/astrodesign.html.

27. Weiss, P., The sun also writhes, *Science News* **153**(13):200-202, 1999.

28. Irion, R., The great eclipse: crown of fire, *New Scientist* **162**(2188):30-33, 1999, discusses rapidly oscillating magnetic waves as a possible energy source.

29. Seeds, M.A., *The Solar System*, 5th edition, Thomson Brooks/Cole, p. 166, 2007.

30. Blondel, P. and Mason, J.W. (Eds.), *Solar System Update*, Praxis, p. 19, 2006.

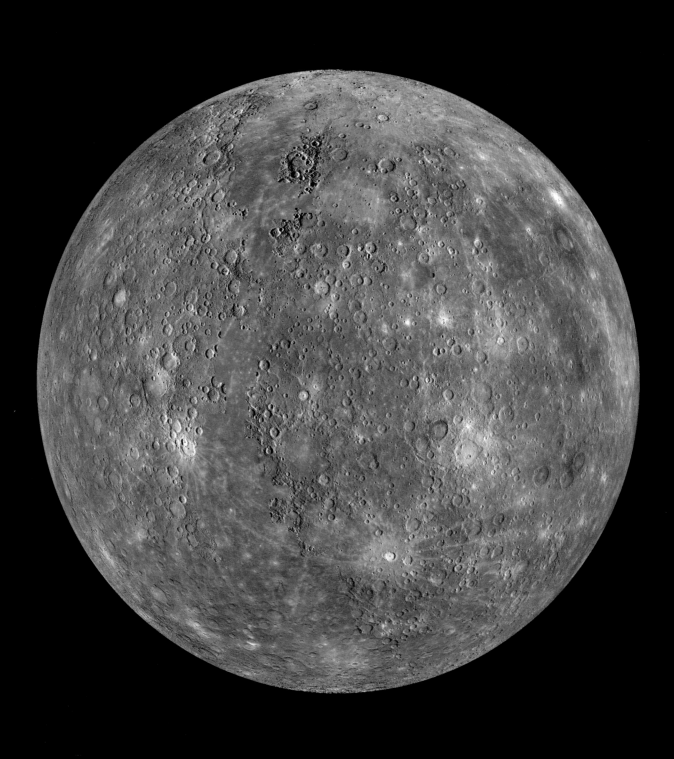

# Chapter 3

# Mercury: The tiny planet that testifies to Creation

Of the eight planets in our solar system, Mercury is the closest to the sun. It is also the smallest, being about one-twentieth the volume of Earth— just a little bigger than Earth's moon. Only Pluto, the furthermost and now downgraded to a 'dwarf planet', is smaller. Even Ganymede (a moon of Jupiter) and Titan (a moon of Saturn) are bigger. Yet, tiny Mercury has much to say about the origin of our solar system, and its many indicators of a young age contradict evolutionist predictions and theories.

**Authors: Andrew Lamb and Spike Psarris[1]**

The English name for the planet comes from the Romans, who named it after the Roman god Mercury, the messenger of the gods.

## Extreme conditions

Mercury is a planet of extremes. As the closest planet to the Sun, Mercury is subject to space weathering (heating, micrometeoroid bombardment, radiation, and solar wind interaction[2]) of extreme intensity.[3] As Mercury very slowly rotates, the part of the planet facing the sun heats up to a temperature of 427°C (more than enough to melt lead), while the reverse side, in the dark, cools to a frigid -173°C. It has virtually no atmosphere to retain heat. This also means that there is little to scatter the sun's rays, so the sky over Mercury is always black. Any visitor to Mercury would be blinded by the close sun, which would be seen as having almost three times the diameter and nine times the area that it does to us on Earth.

The planet has virtually no tilt, so there are no 'seasons', i.e. the northern and southern hemispheres are essentially the same temperature as each other.

Mercury orbits the sun once every 88 Earth days, but takes 58.66 Earth days to rotate once. It thus has the unusual characteristic of rotating on its axis three times for every two complete orbits it makes of the sun.

The gravity on Mercury is 0.378 of Earth's gravity, so if you were on Mercury, you could jump about 2.6 times as high as you could on Earth. You would not see a moon, because, unlike most other planets, Mercury has no moons.

Mercury has a rocky, cratered surface that resembles that of our moon. But Mercury is very different from

**Mercury is the smallest planet in the solar system, as seen here compared to Earth.**

our moon—or any other planet in our solar system—in some fascinating ways. Evolutionary astronomers have long struggled to fit Mercury into their models. And new discoveries have made their problems worse instead of better. Here are some of the challenges.

## Extreme density

For several decades, scientists have known that Mercury is extremely dense. In fact, it has the highest density of all the planets other than Earth. To explain this, Mercury is believed to have an iron core occupying some 75% of its diameter. This extraordinary density has generated much turmoil and confusion in evolutionary astronomy. Evolutionists mostly agree on models of planetary formation … but their models say Mercury can't be anywhere near as dense as it actually is.

Secular scientists used to explain Mercury's density with a large-impact model. They believed that billions of years ago, a large object crashed into Mercury, stripping away its lower-density material, and leaving behind the high-density planet seen today.

Was there any evidence for this collision? Only that otherwise, Mercury would disprove the nebular hypothesis for the solar system's origin.[4] Obviously, this isn't a good standard of evidence. Nevertheless, evolutionists were undeterred, and believed it anyway—until 2011.

In that year, the MESSENGER[5] spacecraft began orbiting Mercury, using its suite of sensors to study Mercury's chemistry, magnetism, atmosphere, geology and landscape. Evolutionists had anticipated Mercury would be "an old burned-out cinder",[6] but to their shock, MESSENGER revealed that Mercury has a lot of volatile (easily vapourized) elements, such as sulfur and potassium. The presence of these elements disproves the large-impact model. If such a collision had occurred, it would have vapourized the volatiles, and they would have escaped into space. But we observe them on Mercury nevertheless.

Now that the large-impact model has been discredited, evolutionists are once again unable to explain one of the most fundamental features of Mercury. As one article noted:

"Mercury's relatively huge metallic core remains a problem. Researchers have some ideas about that, but they still don't have a clue how the planet got

An artist's concept shows the MESSENGER spacecraft in orbit around Mercury. The fuel for its thrusters kept it circling Mercury for four years from 2011 to 2015, when it finally impacted the surface.

so small."[7]

But that's not the only thing about Mercury that evolutionists can't explain.

## Chemical composition

"… not just hellishly hot but apparently covered in brimstone"[8]

Brimstone is an olden-days word for sulfur. As mentioned, volatile elements like sulfur discredit the large-impact explanation for Mercury's density—but they have other implications too. According to evolutionary theories of planetary formation, easily vapourized substances (such as sulfur, water and hydrocarbons) should be very scarce or entirely absent on Mercury, because it is too close to the Sun. There shouldn't be sulfur there, but there is, and *lots*—at least 10, possibly *20 times* as much, proportionally, as on far more distant Earth![9]

"Mercury's interior contains higher abundances of volatile elements than are predicted by several planetary formation models for the innermost planet" concluded the MESSENGER scientists.[10]

"Theorists need to go back to the drawing board on Mercury's formation," said one.[11]

So they did just that. And after demonstrating the inadequacy of evaporation, giant impact, and nebular condensate theories, they now hint timidly at formation from volatile-rich chondritic (stony) meteorites[12] as a means to cope with the uncooperative observed facts.

For evolutionists, "Most previous ideas about Mercury's chemistry are inconsistent with what we have actually measured on the planet's surface."[11] But remnant volatiles on a hot planet pose no problem for a 6,000-year-old solar system.

## Blue hollows

"... this jaw-dropping thing that nobody ever predicted"[13]

Mercury is pockmarked with rashes of irregularly shaped depressions, up to several kilometres across, many having bright bluish halos and interiors. Scientists dub them 'hollows'. They appear 'fresh' and have not accumulated small impact craters, indicating that they are relatively young. Scientists think the hollows form by surface collapse where volatiles escape from rocks.[10]

Those hollows lacking colour and brightness are thought to have exhausted their volatiles, becoming inactive, while the bright, coloured ones are still actively decaying away.[10] "Analysis of the images and estimates of the rate at which the hollows may be growing lead to the conclusion that they are actively forming today".[11]

The hollows occur on crater floors, crater central peaks and crater rim terraces. These are the locations where 'impact melt' ends up when craters form. The intense heat of a meteorite impact melts subsurface rock and splashes it about, forming a layer of molten rock on parts of the crater. Within this layer volatile chemicals may separate into their own distinct mineral layer, which then weathers forming blue hollows.[14,15]

The presence of actively-decaying volatile deposits means the craters cannot be billions of years old, because such geological activity would have ceased eons ago, hence the perplexity of secular planetologists.

## Magnetic field

In 1974–75, the *Mariner 10* spacecraft detected that Mercury had a magnetic field, contradicting evolutionary expectations. If a small planet like Mercury were billions of years old, the secular model says it should no longer have had one. But it does.

Evolutionists addressed this problem by proposing that Mercury's core was not pure iron, as originally believed. They said it must also contain sulfur, which would allow it to stay unfrozen (and supposedly remain able to generate a magnetic field) even over long periods of time.

However, this 'solution' to one problem created another, larger problem. As mentioned earlier, the nebular hypothesis says that Mercury can't contain volatile elements like sulfur. So in trying to explain Mercury's magnetic field with sulfur inside Mercury, evolutionists were discrediting the nebular hypothesis itself—the very idea they were trying to protect. (Somehow, this inconsistency never seemed to be mentioned in the science media's descriptions of Mercury to the public.)

As we saw earlier, MESSENGER has confirmed that Mercury does contain sulfur—lots of it. Although this has increased the conflict between Mercury's observed composition and what the secular model predicted was possible, MESSENGER seemed to solve the puzzle of Mercury's magnetism—or did it?

No, it actually made it worse. When MESSENGER

**Bluish hollows on Mercury's craters are thought to be due to volatile deposits escaping from the rocks. They indicate a young age, as such geological activity should have ceased a very long time ago, if the planet was old.**

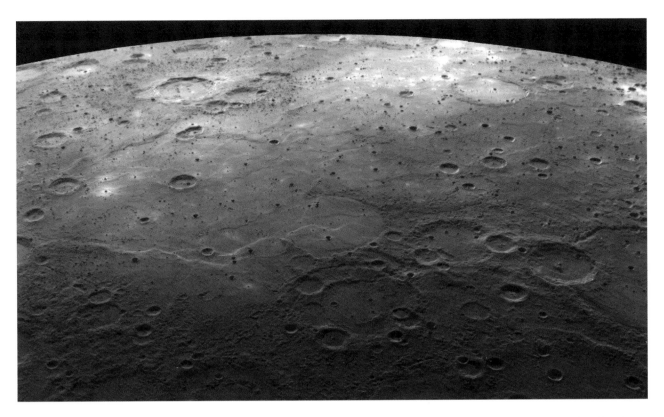

**NASA explains the internal smoothness of these craters on Mercury as being due to lava flows. However, such volcanic activity on such a small planet is an indicator of a young age. Another young age indicator is the fact that the depressions have accumulated very few small impact cavities from meteors, despite Mercury's lack of atmosphere to burn up such meteors.**

first flew by Mercury in 2008–09, the field seemed to have decreased in strength by a few percent. Such a rapid decline would be utterly irreconcilable with millions-of-years scenarios. Did it really decrease?—MESSENGER's 2011 orbit would clear things up …

Indeed, the 2011 measurements revealed a huge *7.8% decrease* in strength since 1975.[16] This decrease is astonishingly fast for something as big as a planet's magnetic field,[16] and shows that the magnetic field, and hence Mercury itself, cannot possibly be billions of years old.

### Evolutionary predictions had proved wrong, but creationist predictions proved correct

Decades ago physicist Dr Russ Humphreys developed a planetary magnetic fields model based on the biblical assumptions that God created the planets 6,000 years ago, and that they began as spheres of water (Genesis 1:2; 2 Peter 3:5). He further supposed that God created the hydrogen atoms of every water molecule with their nuclear spins aligned, forming

a massive magnet, which thenceforth decayed. In 1984, he used this model to predict the magnetic field strengths of Uranus, Neptune and Mercury. His Uranus and Neptune predictions (radically different from evolution-based ones) were demonstrated to be astonishingly accurate when *Voyager II* visited these planets in 1986 and 1989 respectively.[17] And Mercury? Humphreys had predicted a decrease in field strength of 1.8% by 1990, compared to the measured 1974 strength.[18] That would equate to a 4–6% decrease by 2011. So it turns out Mercury's field was decreasing even faster than Dr Humphreys had predicted.[16]

Humphreys had also predicted that older igneous rocks (if any) on Mercury would contain remanent magnetization (i.e. the magnetization that is left behind after an external magnetic field is removed).[18] This prediction was likewise confirmed—Mercury's northern volcanic plains are magnetized, and in the opposite direction to today's field. This indicates that Mercury's magnetic field, like Earth's, was formerly much stronger (sufficient to magnetize surface rock), and has flipped poles at least once.[19]

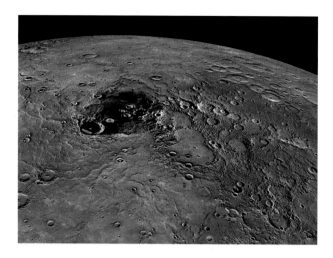

**NASA's radar image of Mercury's north pole; radar-bright areas shown in yellow are thought to contain deposits of water ice.**

### Ice deposits

Scientists had long wondered if patches near Mercury's poles that brightly reflected radar, first detected decades ago using giant radio telescopes on Earth, could be deposits of frozen water.[20] When MESSENGER mapped Mercury's surface the patches were found to correspond to areas of permanent year-round shadow in craters, strengthening the water-ice theory.[21]

MESSENGER's neutron spectrometer detected hydrogen in these patches,[22] strongly supporting the frozen $H_2O$ conclusion.

But even portions of crater floors in permanent shadow receive some reflected light and heat from their crater rims. How could the ice possibly last? Three factors affect water retention in a crater—how close it is to the pole, how big it is, and whether something covers the ice. On Mercury, ice deposits occur even in small craters less than 10 km across, and in craters as far from the pole as latitude 67°—a quarter of the way to the equator![21]

Many of Mercury's ice deposits have thin coverings of dark material, thought to be less-volatile hydrocarbons.[23] However, even with this insulation, "water ice is not stable in craters ≤10 km in diameter located more than 2° from Mercury's pole".[21] As for further away, "Low latitude (<75°) and small (≤10 km in diameter) craters that host radar-bright deposits provide *challenging thermal environments* for water ice"[21] (emphasis added). That is, even in year-round shadow and with an insulating layer it's hard to explain ice enduring for millions of years on a planet where daytime temperatures can melt lead.

# Mercury Facts

| | |
|---|---|
| Mean distance from the sun | 57.9 million km (38.7% Earth's distance) |
| Mass | $0.33 \times 10^{24}$ kg (5.53% Earth) |
| Equatorial radius | 2,440 km (38.3% Earth) |
| Density | 5,427 kg/m³ (98.4% Earth) |
| Gravity | 3.7 m/s² (37.8% Earth) |
| Equatorial escape velocity: | 4.3 km/s (38.4% Earth) |
| Length of Mercury day | 4,222.6 hours or 175.94 Earth days |
| Sidereal rotation period | 1,407.6 hours |
| Orbit around sun (i.e. year): | 88 Earth days |
| Surface temperatures: | 427° C (max.), -173° C (min.), 167° C (mean) |
| Atmosphere | Virtually none, essentially a vacuum. |

Source: Mercury Fact Sheet, NASA, updated 19 April 2016.

## Conclusion

Mercury "doesn't conform to theory" and is "not the planet described in the textbooks".[11]

Good scientific theories should be able to make accurate predictions, but evolutionary expectations about Mercury have been contradicted by observed data. In contrast, creationist theories, such as Dr Russ Humphreys' aligned nuclear spin theory of planetary magnetic field creation, *have* generated accurate predictions about Mercury.[16]

Mercury is geologically active, magnetic, and riddled with volatiles. These youthful characteristics fit comfortably with the Bible's assertion that the heavenly bodies were created on Day 4 (Genesis 1:14), just 6,000 years ago, and are formidably difficult to reconcile with an imagined age of billions of years. Nor can secular models explain Mercury's high density.

Even before MESSENGER, evolutionists had great difficulty accounting for Mercury. One prominent researcher warned his colleagues that any attempt to include Mercury in their evolutionary models will doom the models to failure—he said that Mercury is a "trap" that has "seduced" evolutionists, and has had a "fatal attraction for solar-system modellers".[24] MESSENGER *has only increased these challenges for secular researchers.*

We see that this tiny, seemingly insignificant planet creates enormous stumbling blocks for those who wish to deny the Creator. Truly, "God has chosen the foolish things of the world to confound the wise; and God has chosen the weak things of the world to confound the things which are mighty" (1 Corinthians 1:27).

## References and Notes

1.  This chapter adapted and updated from Lamb, A., *Creation* **34**(4):36–38, 2012; creation.com/mercury2; and Psarris S., *Creation* **26**:(4):36–39, Sept. 2004; creation.com/mercury.
2.  D'Incecco, P. *et al.*, Kuiper Crater on Mercury—an opportunity to study recent surface weathering trends with MESSENGER, 43rd Lunar and Planetary Science Conference, 19–23 March 2012, lpi.usra.edu/meetings/lpsc2012/programAbstracts, accessed 1 June 2012.
3.  Vilas, F. *et al.*, Search for absorption features in Mercury's visible reflectance spectra: recent results from MESSENGER, 43rd LPSC, lpi.usra.edu, 2012.
4.  "The driving force behind previous attempts to account for Mercury has been to fit the high density of the planet into some preferred overall solar system scheme ... . It has become clear that none of these proposed models work, and the high density is conveniently accommodated by the large-impact hypothesis, which makes Mercury unique." Taylor, S.R., *Solar System Evolution: A New Perspective*, Cambridge University Press, New York, p. 307, 2001.
5.  MESSENGER is an acronym of MErcury Surface, Space ENvironment, GEochemistry and Ranging. There were several prior spacecraft visits—three *Mariner 10* fly-bys in 1974–1975 and three MESSENGER fly-bys in 2008–2009.
6.  Kaufman, R., Mercury "hollows" found—pits may be solar system first, nationalgeographic.com, 29 September 2011.
7.  Kerr, R.A., Mercury looking less exotic, more a member of the family, *Science* **333**(6051):1812, 30 September 2011. Notice how secular scientists still assume the nebular hypothesis is correct, and that Mercury formed larger and then somehow 'got small'.
8.  Choi, C.Q., Planet Mercury full of strange surprises, NASA spacecraft reveals, space.com, 29 September 2011.
9.  Nittler, L.R. *et al.*, The major-element composition of Mercury's surface from MESSENGER x-ray spectrometry, *Science* **333**(6051):1847–1850, 30 September 2011.
10. Blewett, D.T. *et al.*, Hollows on Mercury: MESSENGER evidence for geologically recent volatile-related activity, *Science* **333**(6051):1856–1859, 30 September 2011.
11. Mercury not like other planets, MESSENGER finds, Carnegie Institution for Science, carnegiescience.edu, 29 September 2011.
12. Peplowski, P.N. *et al.*, Radioactive elements on Mercury's surface from MESSENGER: implications for the planet's formation and evolution, *Science* **333**(6051):1850–1852, 30 September 2011.
13. MESSENGER science team member David Blewett, quoted in Kaufman, ref. 6.
14. Vaughan, W.M. *et al.*, Hollow-forming layers in impact craters on Mercury: massive sulphide or chloride deposits formed by impact melt differentiation? 43rd LPSC, lpi.usra.edu, 2012.
15. Alternatively, lava from deep underground released by the impact may produce a 'slag' layer which weathers to form the hollows—see Helbert, J. *et al.*, Spectral reflectance measurements of sulphides at the planetary emissivity laboratory—analogs for hollow-forming material on Mercury, 43rd LPSC, lpi.usra.edu, 2012.
16. Humphreys, R., Mercury's magnetic field is fading fast—latest data confirm evidence for a young solar system, *J. Creation* **26**(2):4–6, 2012.
17. Humphreys, R., Beyond Neptune: Voyager II supports Creation, ICR *Impact* #203, May 1990; icr.org/article/329.
18. Humphreys, R., The creation of planetary magnetic fields, *Creation Research Society Quarterly* **21**(3):140–149, December 1984; creationresearch.org/crsq/articles/21/21_3/21_3.html.
19. Purucker, M.E. *et al.*, Evidence for a crustal magnetic signature on Mercury from MESSENGER magnetometer observations, 43rd LPSC, lpi.usra.edu, 2012.
20. Matson, J., New maps of Mercury show icy looking craters on the solar system's innermost planet, scientificamerican.com, 28 March 2012.
21. Chabot, N.L. *et al.*, Craters hosting radar-bright deposits in Mercury's north polar region, 43rd LPSC, lpi.usra.edu, 2012.
22. Lawrence, D.J. *et al.*, Hydrogen at Mercury's north pole? Update on MESSENGER neutron measurements, 43rd LPSC, lpi.usra.edu, 2012.
23. Neumann, G.A. *et al.*, Dark material at the surface of polar crater deposits on Mercury, 43rd LPSC, lpi.usra.edu, 2012.
24. Taylor, S.R., *Destiny or Chance: our solar system and its place in the cosmos*, Cambridge University Press, Cambridge, p. 163, 1998.

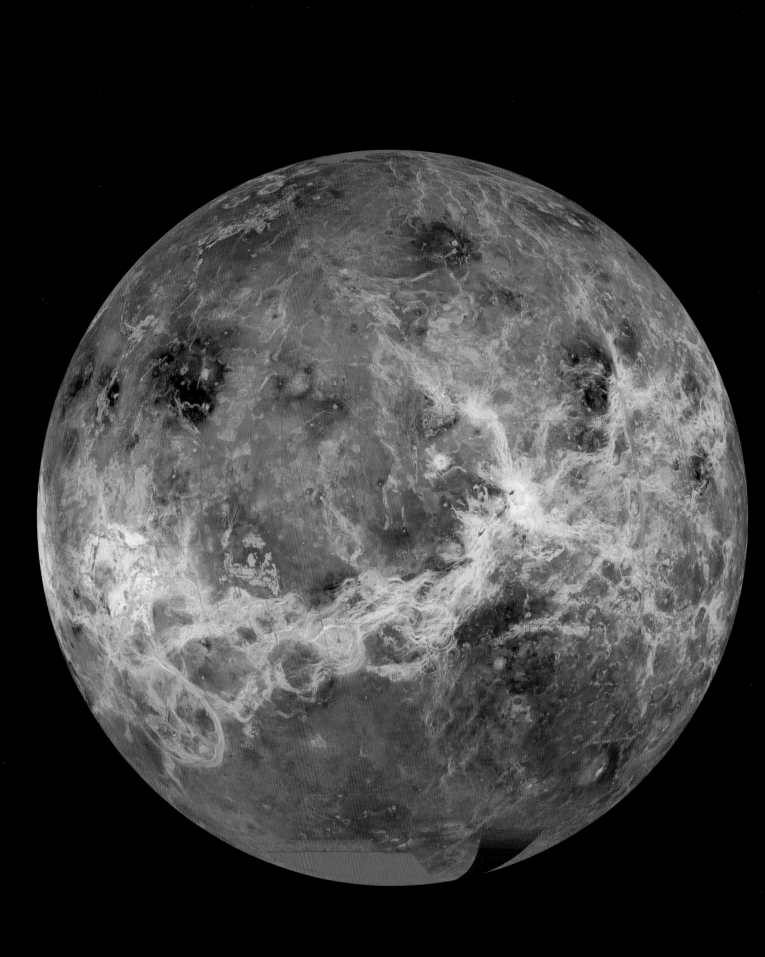

# Chapter 4

# Venus: cauldron of fire

Venus, the second planet from the sun, is often called the 'morning star' and also the 'evening star', since it is the brightest natural object in the sky after the moon, but is visible at night only within about three hours of sunrise and sunset. Venus has the most circular orbit of all the planets, and approaches closest to Earth—42 million km (26 million miles). It is so similar to Earth in many ways that it could be considered our sister planet, but as will be seen there are also huge differences.

**Author: Jonathan Sarfati**[1]

**Venus and Earth are about the same in size, but very different in features, because God designed the one to be habitable and the other not.**

Earth is designed for life, while Venus is about the nearest we have to the medieval descriptions of Hell, so ancient identification of Venus with Lucifer[2] seems inadvertently apt. However, the ancients named it after the Roman goddess of Love.

## Venus's origin according to an eye witness

For the truth about the origin of anything, it helps to have a reliable eyewitness record. Such a record always outweighs any circumstantial evidence that might be interpreted in another way. Genesis claims to be a witness by One who was there—the Creator. Genesis 1:14–19 reads:

> "And God said, 'Let there be lights in the expanse of the heavens to separate the day from the night. And let them be for signs and for seasons, and for days and years, and let them be lights in the expanse of the heavens to give light upon the earth.' And it was so. And God made the two great lights—the greater light to rule the day and the lesser light to rule the night—and the stars. … And there was evening and there was morning, the fourth day."

The Hebrew word for 'star' refers to any bright object in the sky, so includes objects that become 'shooting stars' (meteors), planets of our solar system and, by extension, any planets around other stars.

## Nebular hypothesis or nebulous hypothesis?

Evolutionists believe that our solar system condensed out of a cloud of gas and dust called a nebula, hence the nebular hypothesis. There is no way to reconcile this with the biblically revealed order of events, and there are many scientific problems with the theory as well (see Chapter 1).

Venus provides a major problem—the nebular hypothesis predicts that as the nebula spiralled inwards, all the resulting planets would rotate on their axes in the same direction, i.e. anti-clockwise, called *prograde*. But Venus rotates on its axis in the opposite direction, i.e. clockwise, called *retrograde*. This retrograde motion comes under the definition that its north pole is on the same side of the solar system plane as Earth's north pole. But because some smaller bodies wobble, the poles are defined according to the 'right-hand rule': if you make a 'thumbs-up' gesture with your right hand, imagine that the planet rotates in the direction of that your fingers curl. Then the

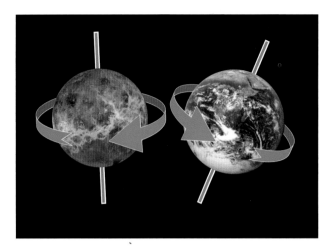

**Most planets rotate on their axes anti-clockwise, i.e. from West to East, or prograde. Venus is the opposite, it rotates from East to West, clockwise, or retrograde, contrary to evolutionary theory.**

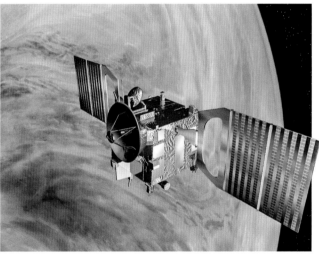

Credit: ESA

**Artist 's concept of the European Space Agency's *Venus Express* satellite in orbit around the atmosphere of Venus. Since 1969 there have been over 40 attempts by the Soviet Union, USA, the European Space Agency, and Japan to send spacecraft to Venus. These have involved skimmers, orbiters, landers, impactors, and probes that obtain flyby gravity-assist to send them on to other planets.**

'North' pole, or more precisely the positive pole, is the direction your thumb is pointing. So some diagrams have the 'North' (positive) pole at the bottom with an axial tilt of 177.3°. But either way, it remains a problem for the nebular hypothesis.

To an observer on Venus, the sun would rise in the west and set in the east. Evolutionists once tried to explain this away by proposing that Venus rotated prograde at first, but it had a bulge, on which

gravitational tidal forces on Earth could act and turn the rotation around. Aside from the weakness of distant tidal forces, which decrease with the *cube* of the distance, it is now known that Venus is even rounder than Earth, so it has no bulge on which Earth could have acted.

A different evolutionary explanation for the retrograde rotation of Venus involves the fact that Venus has no moon. Why not, if Venus was formed by the same natural processes as was Earth, from the same materials, at the same time, in about the same place, according to the evolutionary model? The latest evolutionary explanation is that in the distant past Venus did have a moon, but now it doesn't, due to asteroid collisions—not just one, but two. The first collision formed a moon from Venus debris (for problems, (see Chapter 8 regarding Earth's moon), and the second collision resulted in the retrograde rotation of Venus, which "caused the body of the planet to absorb the moon's orbital energy via tides … . So it spiraled inward until it collided and merged with Venus in a dramatic, last encounter."[3] But there is no verification for any of this, except that if it didn't happen, Venus would pose problems for evolutionary theory. Such supposition does not equate to evidence.

Venus's chemistry is also very different from Earth's. For example, the ratio of the isotopes of the inert gas argon (used to fill light bulbs), i.e. $^{36}Ar$ to $^{40}Ar$, is 300 times greater on Venus than on Earth. If the nebular hypothesis were correct, then it would mean a vastly different nebular composition in the region of Venus, and such differences are implausible in a relatively small region of a nebula.

## Magnetic field evidence for Creation

Another problem for evolutionary theories about the planets is their magnetic fields. As shown in Chapter 5, Earth's magnetic field is a good example of design, and the field's decay (as well as the evidence for rapid magnetic field reversals) is excellent evidence for a young Earth. But no spacecraft has detected any magnetic field on Venus, and the sensitivity of the instruments places an upper limit on any magnetic field of 25,000 times weaker than Earth's.

Evolutionists believe that planetary magnetic fields are explained by self-sustaining dynamos, so they

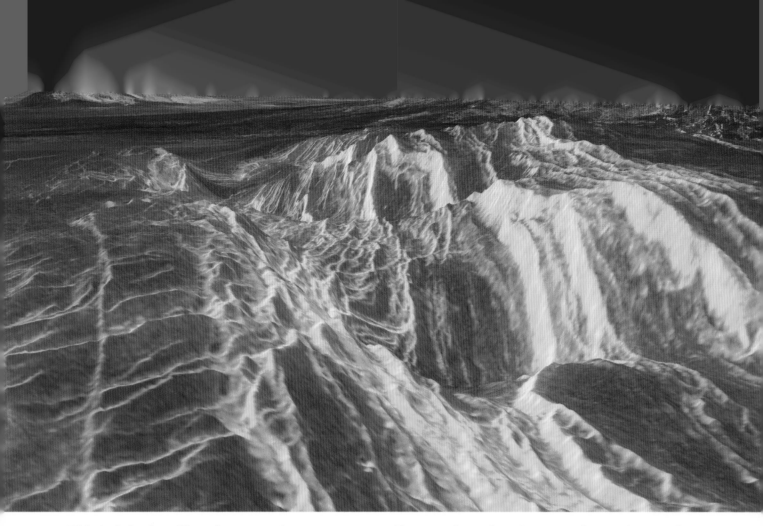

**With the help of satellite radar scans and computer-generated imagery, the surface of Venus can be seen here as a hot, inhospitable place, incapable of supporting life.**

explain the problem of Venus's missing magnetic field by its much slower rotation (243 Earth days for one sidereal rotation). But Mercury also rotates slowly (58.65 days), yet its field is clearly measurable, while Mars rotates almost as fast as Earth (1.025 days), but its field is less than 1/10,000 of Earth's. However, the theory of the creationist physicist Dr Russell Humphreys explains all the data.[4] When all the planets' cores were formed, they started off with a magnetic field produced by a decaying electrical current. The smaller the core and the poorer electrical conductor its material was, the faster the field would decay. It is thought that Venus has a smaller and less conductive core than Earth, so the field is now very weak, just as the Humphreys model suggests.

## Young and fresh

Venus provides yet another problem for billions-of-years beliefs: its surface, as shown from radar images from the *Magellan* satellite, seems very fresh. There are high mountains including Maxwell Montes (11,000 m or 36,000 ft above the mean surface level), rift valleys including one 9,000 km (5,600 miles) long, shield volcanoes, steep slopes, large rocks and smooth plains. There is no evidence for millions of years of erosion, although the thick atmosphere and huge atmospheric temperature differences would be expected to whip up huge sand and dust storms.

There are also circular structures thought to be impact craters, but the mystery is that there are many fewer—only 935—than predicted by evolutionary theories.[5] They are also fairly uniformly distributed. So evolutionists propose that the *whole surface was recycled* due to volcanic and tectonic activity.[5] They claim that the resurfacing ceased 800–300 million years ago, yet 84% of the craters show no sign of modification.[5] R. Stephen Saunders, Project Scientist at NASA, makes these remarkable admissions:

"All the surface appeared to be about the same age and geologically young. … Curiously, this debate about Venus echoes a debate among early geologists a couple of hundred years ago. The catastrophists believed that most of Earth's rocks formed over a short period of time in the Noachian floods, while the uniformitarianists held that 'the present is the key to the past.' In other words, geologic time was vast, and enormous surface modifications result from slow changes that we can see operating today. In that early historic debate, the uniformitarianists ultimately won out. For Venus, in the opinion of this writer, the catastrophe model will in time be judged more nearly correct than the equilibrium model. ... The geologic rule of uniformitarianism—'the present is the key to the past'—does not apply to Venus in the long-term sense."[6]

But we would go further: the evidence from *both* Venus and Earth point to catastrophism. In the case of Earth, the catastrophe really *was* the Flood of Noah's day, unjustly rejected.

For Venus, the evidence seems best explained by recent cratering episodes during Creation Week or the Flood, as proposed by creationist astronomers Dr Danny Faulkner and Wayne Spencer.[7]

## Changing shape

When Galileo (1564–1642) looked through the newly-invented telescope, he discovered that Venus has phases like our moon. But the moon is always brightest when it is full, where we see light reflected from a whole hemisphere, and dimmer when it's in a crescent phase where we see light reflected only from a tiny fraction of the surface. However, the brightness of Venus doesn't change that much. Galileo realized that, unlike the moon, which orbits the earth, Venus orbits the sun.[8] Thus the 'full Venus' occurs when Venus is on the opposite side of the sun from the earth; the extra surface reflection is counterbalanced by the far greater distance. The 'crescent Venus' is actually brighter than the full Venus because it is so much closer to us.

The time taken for Venus to be seen again from the earth in the same position with respect to the sun (i.e. to return to the same orientation towards Earth, e.g. between one full Venus and the next), is called the phase cycle or *synodic* period. Showing that so-called primitive cultures were nothing of the kind, the Mayans of South America calculated the synodic period of Venus to be 584 Earth days, incredibly close to the modern scientific figure of 583.92 days,[9] and they did so without telescopes and (probably) without realizing that Venus orbits the sun. Note: this is not to be confused with the *sidereal* period, the time for one complete orbit of Venus around the sun, relative

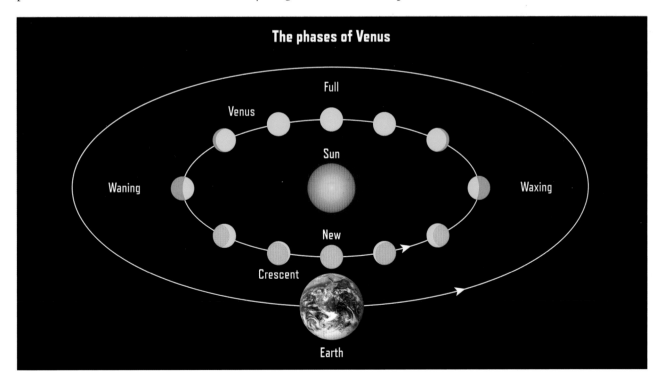

**Galileo was the first person to observe the phases of Venus, in 1610, with the newly invented telescope. He concluded that these phases could only be explained if Venus orbited the sun, not the earth.**

to an observer outside the solar system, which is 224.7 Earth days. This is consistent with the purpose of the heavenly bodies given in Genesis 1:14.

## So similar, yet so different

As shown in 'Venus Facts', Venus and Earth are almost the same in size, density and gravity, and Venus is almost three-quarters of Earth's distance from the sun. Yet this seemingly small difference in distance makes a huge difference to the temperature.

Earth is at an ideal distance from the sun (see Chapter 6), and also has an atmosphere that provides a greenhouse effect, mainly due to water vapour, but also to carbon dioxide ($CO_2$). This means that most of the earth is in the narrow temperature range that allows water to be *liquid*. It is the only place in the universe *known* to have liquid water, aside from the possibility that Jupiter's moon Europa has an underground ocean, and Saturn's moon Enceladus might also have liquid water. There has also been speculation of underground oceans on Titan and Triton.

Conversely, Venus, only a little closer to the sun, was hot enough to drive out $CO_2$ from carbonate rocks (e.g. limestone) and so has had a *runaway* greenhouse effect, of a type that could never happen on Earth. It has a thick atmosphere of 96.5% $CO_2$, with a small

The atmosphere of Venus is mostly carbon dioxide. Traces of sulfur dioxide and water vapour in this atmosphere combine to form thick hot opaque clouds of sulfuric acid, which completely cover the planet, including the poles. Surface images of a hot Venus are obtained by using radar to penetrate these clouds.

amount of nitrogen, and a pressure 92 times that of our own atmosphere, or as much pressure as at a depth of one kilometre in Earth's oceans. This results in a surface hot enough to glow red and melt lead. None of the large organic molecules required for life would stand a chance.

Also, the thick clouds reflect 76% of sunlight, which is why it is so bright. They appear slightly yellow because of some chemicals that absorb a little blue light. But the clouds mean that very little sunlight reaches the surface, although the *Venera 9* and *10* spacecrafts were able to take photographs. However, the atmosphere is so thick that light bends markedly, so that an observer (extremely well protected!) on Venus would see some light even at night. Even more amazingly, the atmosphere would bend the light so much that an observer in any location could see the entire surface of Venus—it would seem like being at the bottom of a vast bowl.

If that weren't enough, the clouds do not comprise water droplets like Earth's, but instead contain some concentrated sulfuric acid ($H_2SO_4$) droplets, and possibly some ferric chloride ($FeCl_3$) crystals.

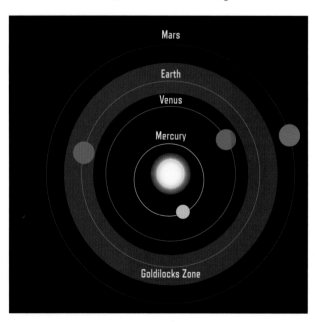

Earth is in the 'Goldilocks Zone': not too hot, not too cold, just right—for life.

# Venus Facts

| | |
|---|---|
| Mean distance from sun | $108.2 \times 10^6$ km (0.723 AU, i.e. 72.3% Earth's distance) |
| Mass | $4.87 \times 10^{24}$ kg (81.5% Earth) |
| Equatorial radius | 6,051.8 km (94.9% Earth) |
| Mean density | 5,243 kg/m$^3$ (95.1% Earth) |
| Surface gravity | 8.87 m/s$^2$ (90.5% Earth) |
| Escape velocity | 10.36 km/sec (92.6% Earth) |
| Length of Venus day | 2,802 hours or 116.75 Earth days |
| Sidereal rotation period | -5,832.6 hours or -243.7 Earth days (- means retrograde) |
| Orbit around sun (i.e. year) | 224.7 Earth days (61.5% Earth year) |
| Atmospheric composition | 96.5% $CO_2$, 3.5% $N_2$, traces $SO_2$, Ar, $H_2O$, CO, He, Ne |
| Average temperature | 464 °C |
| Obliquity to orbit (tilt) | 177.36° (cf. Earth 23.44°) |
| Unlike most other planets, Venus has no moons | |

Source: Venus Fact Sheet, NASA, updated 19 April 2016.

## Conclusion

Venus is a beautiful-looking heavenly object, created as a sign and a marker of times, and provides a huge stumbling block against evolutionary theories. But the outward beauty hides an almost unimaginably harsh interior, and teaches us how finely God tuned Earth's orbit to support life.

## References and Notes

1. This chapter adapted and updated from Sarfati, J., *Creation* **23**(3):30–34, 2001; creation.com/venus.
2. Jerome, who produced the Vulgate, the major Latin translation of the Bible, translated the Hebrew word *heylel* in Isaiah 14:12 as "Lucifer", although it simply means 'morning star' or 'star of the morning'. Lucifer literally means 'light-bearer' and is one name of the angelic being who fell and became Satan (= 'adversary'). Some older English translations reflect the Vulgate influence in this verse.
3. Tytell, D., Why doesn't Venus have a moon? 10 October 2006, skyandtelescope.com/news/4353026.html.
4. Humphreys, D.R., The creation of planetary magnetic fields, *Creation Research Society Quarterly* **21**(3):140–149, December 1984; creationresearch.org/crsq/articles/21/21_3/21_3.html.
5. *Face of Venus Website:* 3.0 Impact Craters, eps.mcgill.ca/~bud/craters/venus_impact.html.
6. Beatty, J.K. *et al.* (Eds.), *The New Solar System*, 4th ed., Sky Publishing Corporation and Cambridge University Press, pp. 99, 110, 1999.
7. See their exchange in *J. Creation* **14**(1):46–49, 2000; creation.com/response-to-faulkners-biblically-based-cratering-theory for similarities and differences in their proposals, and the references to their papers therein.
8. For information about Galileo's dispute with the Roman Catholic church and how his theories conflicted with Greek philosophy rather than the Bible, see Grigg, R., The Galileo 'twist' *Creation* **19**(4):30–32, September 1997; creation.com/gal-twist, and Schirrmacher, T., The Galileo affair: history or heroic hagiography, *J. Creation* **14**(1):91–100, 2000; creation.com/gal-affair.
9. Cardno, S., The mystery of ancient man, *Creation* **20**(2):10–13, March 1998; creation.com/pyramids.

# Chapter 5

# Earth is 'too special'?

Earth is the third planet from the sun. Of the four terrestrial (i.e. rocky or non-gas) planets (Mercury, Venus, Earth and Mars), it is the largest in size, mass, and density, and has the highest surface gravity, the strongest magnetic field, and the fastest rotation. It is the only planet to have liquid water, and is exactly the right distance from the sun to obtain the heat and light that life on Earth needs. It is not surprising that Earth is the only place in the universe where life is known to exist.

**Author: Jonathan Sarfati**[1]

## So much water!

About 71% of planet Earth is covered in water. Evolution models say all this water shouldn't be here, because volatile gases couldn't have condensed in the inner solar system so close to the sun, but were blown outwards instead. Evolutionists have proposed that the earth's water was delivered by a large bombardment of comets. However, this explanation no longer looks tenable. Comets Halley, Hyakutake, and Hale-Bopp have all been shown to contain 'heavy' water, with much more deuterium than Earth's water has.

Comet Wild 2 was even more surprising—it contains high-temperature minerals which, according to the nebular hypothesis (Chapter 1), were formed very close to the sun, where there could be no water at all to comprise the comet. Many evolutionists now acknowledge that, according to their models, Earth should not have any water. "There's one thing on which most geochemists and astronomers agree: The celestial pantry is now empty of a key ingredient in the recipe for Earth."[2]

Nearly 75% of the continental land has a crust of sedimentary rock (which is evidence for Noah's Flood). Earth's atmosphere is ~78% oxygen, ~21% nitrogen, 0.93% argon as well as water vapour, carbon dioxide, methane and ozone—the greenhouse gases which keep Earth's temperature favourable for life.

## Evidence that the earth is special

Astronomer Thomas Clarke of the University of Central Florida in Orlando recently made an astonishing statement: "It's a bit depressing to think that Earth-like planets are too special."[3]

Why should this be 'depressing'? Those who believe the Bible should be elated—after all, the earth was created first (before the sun, moon and stars) and was specially designed to accommodate millions of kinds of living things. See Conditions for life, Chapter 6.

First, one must understand that evolutionary astronomers have excluded a Creator by decree, and instead believe that our solar system formed by itself:

> "Astronomers agree that the planets and moons of our Solar System formed in a swirling disc of dust and gas around the Sun. … And in the inner regions, dusty particles melted and stuck together, forming hot blobs of rock that cooled and merged

to make Mercury, Venus, Earth and Mars."[3]

That is, according to evolutionists, the solar system was born in a collapsing cloud of dust and gas called a *nebula*, hence the term *nebular hypothesis*. Most of this collapsed into the sun (with a major problem that the planets have most of the solar system's angular momentum—see Chapter 1), while the inner planets were formed from fragments that collided and fused together.

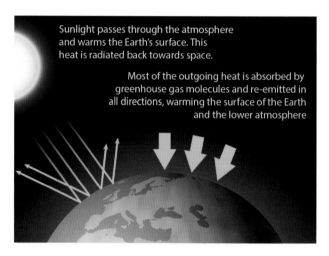

**Earth's atmosphere contains greenhouse gases—primarily water vapour plus much smaller amounts of carbon dioxide, methane and nitrous oxide—which act as a thermal blanket, absorbing heat and warming the surface to a life-supporting average of 15° C (59° F).**

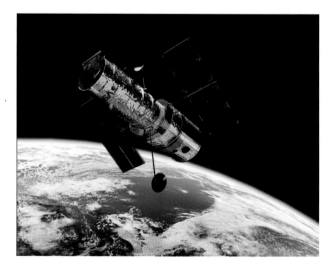

**Earth, seen here with the *Hubble Space Telescope* in orbit, is unique among all the planets in the solar system. Its distance from the sun, temperature range allowing liquid water, and diverse range of organic life, all point to an Intelligent Designer who created the earth as a very special place, ideal for life.**

dit: C. Mayhew & R. Simmon (NASA/GSFC), NOAA/ NGDC, DMSP

**Composite map of Earth's city lights made from multiple night-time images taken as spacecraft flew over the various countries.**

However, the more scientists have investigated this, the more they have realized that there is a problem. There was no reason for any rocky particles to melt—what would have heated them? If anything, back then the sun would have been cooler than today (see Chapter 2). Therefore only a small and very-close-to-the-sun planet like Mercury could conceivably have become hot enough. But further from the sun, they have a problem: Nobody can figure out how to get 1-km planetesimals from grains of dust.

> "While asteroid-sized rocks would have aggregated in the inner Solar System, they would not have

**Asteroid 2013 TX68, a 30 m (100 ft) rock discovered in 2013 flew past Earth on March 7 2016 at the very safe distance of 4 million km (2.5 million miles), about 10 times the distance from Earth to the moon. Earth is protected from most asteroid impacts by the intense gravity of Jupiter, the largest planet in the solar system (see Chapter 10).**

melted and clumped together to form planets. ... the solid rocks would simply zoom past each other or collide and recoil like snooker balls."[3]

Evolutionary astronomers propose that a supernova explosion within 50 light years from Earth supplied the nebula with radioactive aluminium-26, which provided heat as it decayed. But this requires a highly unlikely set of coincidences, which is why the chances are "very much against the odds".[3]

However, Dr Clarke couldn't bear the thought of Earth being in a favoured place in the universe, even in an evolutionary scenario, as shown in the quote at the beginning of this section. It has a great deal to do with the humanistic/atheistic belief that life on Earth, including humanity, just 'happened'. Therefore they would expect our Earth to be neither especially equipped nor to occupy a special location in the universe. So he prefers the above "speculative"[3] idea!

## Hidden assumptions of secular cosmology

This denial of Earth's special place goes even further, and it underlies the big bang theory itself. Most people don't realize that this theory depends on a philosophical *assumption* called the *Cosmological Principle*—that there is no special place or direction in the universe. That is, the universe has no centre and no edge to it.[4]

However, consistent with the Bible, we can start

**Earth is very special; it is the only place known to support life.**

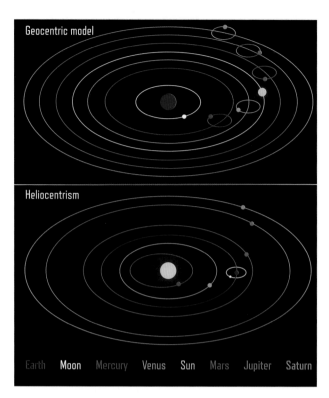

**In the old geocentric model, Earth was at the centre of the universe with the planets and sun revolving around it in circles. In the heliocentric model, the sun is at the centre of our solar system, and the planets revolve around the sun in elliptical orbits.**

from a different assumption—that humanity *is* special in God's sight, and Earth, as our home, *does* show evidences of uniqueness, including its location. Both a centred and a centreless universe are *consistent with* the observation that almost all galaxies are receding from Earth, so the choice is purely *philosophical* on those grounds.[5] But only the idea that our galaxy is near the centre of the universe fits *all* the evidence, making sense of the quantized redshifts that a centreless universe has great difficulties explaining.[6]

## Galactocentrism, not geocentrism

Geocentrism was the view of ancient Greek philosophers, who believed that the earth was at rest in the centre of the cosmos, with all the stars and planets revolving around it. They believed that the heavenly bodies were contained in spheres of varying size, which moved with perfect geometric precision.

Galactocentrism is the model indicated by the 'stretching' of starlight towards the red end of the spectrum (or 'redshift'),[7] in which the earth is not fixed at the centre, but close to it. The vast cosmos stretches out symmetrically around us. But it is not infinite; only God is. So if one kept travelling far enough away from Earth, one would eventually come to an 'edge'.

Copernicus and Galileo challenged the scientific establishment of their day by proposing that the earth orbited the sun, i.e the heliocentric view.[8] Skeptics have claimed that these men showed long ago that the earth has no central place in the cosmos, and that

we should not try to reintroduce this 'outmoded' idea. First, this is anachronistic—in their time, the centre was the worst place to be, while the heavens were considered to be perfect. So removing Earth to the third place around the sun was actually considered to be a promotion, not a demotion. Second, for skeptics to invoke Copernicus does their cause little good. He felt that the sun was at, or close to, the centre of the universe, and both of these men also affirmed belief in God as Creator and His authorship of Scripture.[9] Galactocentrism would seem to be a very natural modification and extension of the Copernican view of the heavens.

## Conclusion

Of course, there is nothing depressing about God creating Earth especially for life, as the Bible says! The genuine scientific evidence, as opposed to unscientific assumptions, is just another confirmation that nothing in real science contradicts the Bible—on the contrary it confirms the Bible's history over and over again.

# The earth's magnetic field: evidence that the earth is young

Earth has a magnetic field pointing almost north-south—only 11.5° off. This is an excellent design feature of our planet: it enables navigation by compasses, and it also shields us from dangerous charged particles from the sun. It is also powerful evidence that the earth must be as young as the Bible teaches.

In the 1970s, the creationist physics professor Dr Thomas Barnes noted that measurements since 1835 have shown that the field is decaying at 5% per century.[10] This equates to losing almost half its energy every 1,400 years, i.e. 1,400 years ago it was twice as strong, and so on. (In fact, archeological measurements show that the field was 40% stronger in AD 1000 than today[11]). Barnes, the author of a well-regarded electromagnetism textbook,[12] proposed that the earth's magnetic field was caused by a *decaying electric current* in the earth's metallic core. This decay would also be exponential as electromagnetic theory predicts. Barnes calculated that the current could not have been decaying for more than 10,000 years, or else its original strength would have been large enough to melt the earth. So the earth must be younger than that.

## Evolutionist responses

The decaying current model is obviously incompatible with the billions of years needed by evolutionists. So their preferred model is a *self-sustaining dynamo* (electric generator). The earth's rotation and convection is supposed to circulate the molten nickel/iron of the outer core. Positive and negative charges in this liquid metal are supposed to circulate unevenly, producing an electric current, thus generating the magnetic field. But scientists have not produced a workable model despite half a century of research, and there are many problems.[13]

But the major criticism of Barnes' young-earth argument concerns evidence that the magnetic field has *reversed* many times—i.e. compasses would have pointed south instead of north. When grains of the common magnetic mineral *magnetite* in volcanic lava or ash flows cool below its *Curie point* of 570° C (1060° F),[14] the magnetic domains partly align themselves

A 'force-field' around the earth. The earth's magnetism is running down. This world-wide phenomenon could not have been going on for more than a few thousand years, despite swapping direction many times. Evolutionary theories are not able to explain properly how the magnetism could sustain itself for billions of years.

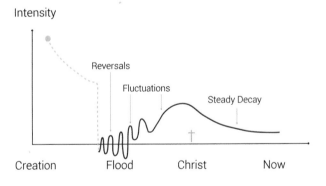

How the earth's magnetic field has changed. The intensity could not have been much higher than the starting point shown, indicating a young age.

in the direction of the earth's magnetic field *at that time*. Once the rock has fully cooled, the magnetite's alignment is fixed. Thus we have a permanent record of the earth's field through time.

Although evolutionists have no good explanations for the reversals, they maintain that, because of them, the straightforward decay assumed by Dr Barnes is invalid. Also, their model requires at least thousands of years for a reversal. And with their dating assumptions, they believe that the reversals occur at intervals of millions of years, and point to an old Earth.

The Aurora Borealis (Northern Lights) as seen by NASA astronaut Scott Kelly aboard the International Space Station 350 km above the earth. This effect is caused by charged particles from space striking the earth's atmosphere and then being deflected towards the poles by the earth's magnetic field (which also diverts many such particles harmlessly back into space).

## Creationist counter-response[15]

The creationist physicist Dr Russell Humphreys believed that Dr Barnes had the right idea, and he also accepted that the reversals were real. He modified Barnes' model to account for special effects of a liquid conductor, like the molten metal of the earth's outer core. If the liquid flowed upwards (due to convection—hot fluids rise, cold fluids sink) this could sometimes make the field reverse quickly.[16,17] Creationist geophysicist Dr John Baumgardner proposes that the plunging of tectonic plates was a cause of the Genesis Flood and rapid continental drift (more like a sprint).[18] Dr Humphreys says these plates would have sharply cooled the outer parts of the core, driving the convection.[19] This means that most of the reversals occurred in the Flood year, every week or two. And after the Flood, there would be large fluctuations due to residual motion. But the reversals and fluctuations could not halt the overall decay pattern—rather, the total field energy would decay even faster (see diagram).[20]

This model also explains why the sun reverses its magnetic field every 11 years. The sun is a gigantic ball of hot, energetically moving, electrically conducting gas. Contrary to the dynamo model, the overall field energy of the sun is decreasing.

Dr Humphreys also proposed a test for his model: magnetic reversals should be found in rocks known to have cooled in days or weeks. For example, in a thin lava flow, the outside would cool first, and record earth's magnetic field in one direction; the inside would cool later, and record the field in another direction.

Three years after this prediction, leading researchers Robert Coe and Michel Prévot found a thin lava layer that must have cooled within 15 days, and had 90° of reversal recorded continuously in it.[21] And it was no fluke—eight years later, they reported an even faster reversal.[22] This was staggering news to them and the rest of the evolutionary community, but strong support for Humphreys' model. (See also Humphreys, D.R. and de Spain, N.J., Earth's mysterious magnetism and that of other celestial orbs, CRSB, 2015 (e-book).

Creationist Russell Humphreys' predictions for the magnetic field strengths of Uranus and Neptune were confirmed by *Voyager 2* when it flew past these planets in 1986 and 1989.

## Conclusion

The earth's magnetic field is not only a good navigational aid and a shield from space particles, it is powerful evidence against evolution and billions of years. The clear decay pattern shows the earth could not be older than about 10,000 years.

# Origin of the Earth's magnetic field: The Humphreys Proposal

Dr Humphreys proposed that God first created the earth out of water.[23] He based this on several Scriptures, e.g. 2 Peter 3:5 which states that the earth was formed out of water and by water. After this, God would have transformed much of the water into other substances like rock minerals. Now water contains hydrogen atoms, and the nucleus of a hydrogen atom is a tiny magnet. Normally these magnets cancel out, so water as a whole is almost non-magnetic. But Humphreys proposed that God created the water with the nuclear magnets aligned. Immediately after creation, they would have formed a more random arrangement, which would have caused the earth's magnetic field to decay. This would generate current in the core, which would then decay according to Barnes' model, apart from many reversals in the Flood year as Humphreys' model states.

## Observational support from the fields of other planets

Dr Humphreys also calculated the fields of other planets (and the sun) based on this model. The important factors are the mass of the object, the size of the core and how well it conducts electricity, plus the assumption that their original material was water. His model explains features which are deep puzzles to dynamo theorists. For example, evolutionists refer to "the enigma of lunar magnetism"[24]—the moon once had a strong magnetic field, although it rotates only about once a month. Also, according to evolutionary models of its origin, it never had a *molten* core, necessary for a dynamo to work. Also, Mercury has a far stronger magnetic field than dynamo theory expects from a planet rotating 59 times slower than Earth.

Even more importantly, in 1984, Dr Humphreys made some predictions of the field strengths of Uranus and Neptune, the two giant gas planets beyond Saturn. His predictions were about 100,000 times the evolutionary dynamo predictions. The two rival models were inadvertently put to the test when the *Voyager 2* spacecraft flew past these planets in 1986 and 1989. The fields for Uranus and Neptune[25] were just as Humphreys had predicted.[26] Yet many anti-creationists call creation 'unscientific' because it supposedly makes no predictions! His theories have also been vindicated for Mercury.[27]

Humphreys' model also explains why the moons of Jupiter that have cores have magnetic fields, while Callisto, which lacks a core, also lacks a field.[28,29]

## Cause of the earth's magnetic field

Materials like iron are composed of tiny *magnetic domains*, which each behave like tiny magnets. The domains themselves are composed of even tinier atoms, which are themselves microscopic magnets, lined up within the domain. Normally the domains cancel each other out. But in magnets, like a compass needle, more of the domains are lined up in the same direction, and so the material has an overall magnetic field.

Earth's core is mainly iron and nickel, so could its magnetic field be caused the same way as a compass needle's? No—above a temperature called the *Curie point*, the magnetic domains are disrupted. The earth's

# Earth Facts

| | |
|---|---|
| Mean distance from sun | $149.6 \times 10^6$ km (= 1 Astronomical Unit AU) |
| Mass | $5.97 \times 10^{24}$ kg (1/330,000 × sun, 81.3 × moon) |
| Equatorial radius | 6,378.137 km |
| Density | 5,514 kg/m$^3$ |
| Surface gravity | 9.798 m/s$^2$ |
| Earth's axis tilt | 23.44º (this results in Earth's seasons) |
| Equatorial escape velocity | 11.186 km/sec |
| Length of Earth day | 24 hours |
| Sidereal rotation period | 23.9345 hours |
| Orbit around the sun (year) | 365.242 days |
| Average temperature | 15º C |
| Atmosphere (dry air) | $N_2$ 78.08%, $O_2$ 20.95%, $H_2O$ ~1%, $CO_2$ 0.04% (400 ppm), + traces of Ar, Ne, He, and CH4 |

Source: Earth Fact Sheet, NASA, updated 19 April 2106.

core at its coolest region is about 3,400–4,700° C (6,150–8,500° F), much hotter than the Curie points of all known substances.

But in 1820, the Danish physicist H.C. Ørsted discovered that an electric current produces a magnetic field. Without this, there could be no electric motors. So could an electric current be responsible for the earth's magnetic field? Electric motors have a power source, but electric currents normally decay almost instantly once the power source is switched off (except in superconductors). So how could there be an electric current inside the earth, without a source?

The great creationist physicist Michael Faraday answered this question in 1831 with his discovery that a changing magnetic field *induces* an electric voltage, the basis of electrical generators.

Imagine the earth soon after creation with a large electrical current in its core. This would produce a strong magnetic field. Without a power source, this current would decay. Thus the magnetic field would decay too. As decay is change, it would induce a current, lower but in the same direction as the original one.

So we have a decaying current producing a decaying field which generates a decaying current … . If the circuit dimensions are large enough, the current would take a while to die out. The decay rate can be accurately calculated, and is always exponential (linear decays are rare in nature).[30] The electrical energy doesn't disappear—it is turned into heat, a process discovered by the creationist physicist James Joule in 1840. And a current in a large sphere will decay more slowly than one in a small sphere.

This is the basis of Dr Barnes' model.

## Conclusion

The earth's magnetic field is not only a good navigational aid and a shield from space particles, it is powerful evidence against evolution and billions of years. The clear decay pattern shows the earth is young, as the Bible clearly reveals.

## References and Notes

1.  This chapter adapted and updated from Sarfati, J., *Creation* **28**(3):43–44, 2006. creation.com/earth-is-too-special.
2.  Harder, B., Water for The Rock: Did Earth's oceans come from the heavens? *Science News* **161**(12):184, 23 March 2002.

3.  Reported by Muir, H., in: Earth was a freak, *New Scientist* **177**(2388):24, 29 March 2003.

4.  Not to be confused with the notion of an infinite universe, which most big-bangers reject. The two-dimensional surface of a balloon is also finite, despite having neither centre nor edge.

5.  Even Edwin Hubble, the discoverer of the expansion of the universe, admitted, "Such a condition [redshifts] would imply that we occupy a unique position in the universe … . But the unwelcome supposition of a favored location must be avoided at all costs. … is intolerable; moreover, it represents a discrepancy with the theory because the theory postulates homogeneity." *The Observational Approach to Cosmology*, Clarendon, Oxford, pp. 50, 51 and 59, 1937.

6.  This refers to regular 'spacings' in the 'shift' in the frequency (hence colour) of their light, and hence the distances assigned to faraway galaxies. See Humphreys, R., Our galaxy is the centre of the universe, 'quantized' redshifts show, *J. Creation* **16**(2):95–104, 2002; creation.com/centre.

7.  See Demick, D., and Wieland, C., In the middle of the action, *Creation* **20**(1):53–55, December 2005; creation.com/quantized.

8.  Sarfati, J., Galileo Quadricentennial: Myth vs fact, *Creation* **31**(3):49–51, 2009; creation.com/gal-400.

9.  Knight, D.C., *Copernicus: titan of modern astronomy*, Franklin Watts Inc., New York, p. 198, 1965. Copernicus said, "At last I began to chafe that philosophers could by no means agree upon any one certain theory of the mechanism of the Universe, wrought for us by a supremely good and orderly Creator … ."

10. McDonald, K.L. and Gunst, R.H., An analysis of the earth's magnetic field from 1835 to 1965, *ESSA Technical Report, IER 46-IES 1*, U.S. Govt. Printing Office, Washington, 1967.

11. Merrill R.T. and McElhinney, M.W., *The Earth's Magnetic Field*, Academic Press, London, pp. 101–106, 1983.

12. Barnes, T.G., *Foundations of Electricity and Magnetism*, 3rd ed., El Paso, Texas, 1977.

13. Measurements of electrical currents in the sea floor pose difficulties for the most popular class of dynamo models—Lanzerotti, L.J., *et al.*, Measurements of the large-scale direct-current earth potential and possible implications for the geomagnetic dynamo, *Science* **229**(4708):47–49, 1986. Also, the measured rate of field decay is sufficient to generate the current needed to produce today's field strength, meaning that there is no dynamo operating today, if it ever did.

14. The Curie point, or Curie tenperature, is the temperature at which certain materials lose their permanent magnetic properties, to be replaced by induced magnetism.

15. More details can be found at creation.com/magfield, under the Addendum.

16. D.R. Humphreys, Reversals of the earth's magnetic field during the Genesis Flood, *Proceedings of the First International Conference on Creationism*, Creation Science Fellowship, Pittsburgh, **2**:113–126, 1986; see icr.org/article/reversals-magnetic-field-flood. The moving conductive liquid would carry magnetic flux lines with it, and this would generate new currents, producing new flux in the opposite direction. See also the interview of Humphreys in *Creation* **15**(3):20–23, 1993; creation.com/humphreys2.

17. Humphreys, D.R., Physical mechanism for reversals of the earth's magnetic field during the flood, *Proceedings of the Second International Conference on Creationism*, Creation Science Fellowship, Pittsburgh, **2**:129–142, 1990. Dr Barnes, who had opposed field reversals because no mechanism could be demonstrated, responded (p. 141): "Dr Humphreys has come up with a novel and physically sound approach to reversals of the magnetic field."

18. Dr Baumgardner's papers can be found at globalflood.org, while a summary is in *The Creation Answers Book*, Ch. 11.

19. Humphreys, D.R., Discussion of J. Baumgardner, Numerical simulation of the large-scale tectonic changes accompanying the Flood, *Proceedings of the First International Conference on Creationism*, Creation Science Fellowship, Pittsburgh, **2**:29, 1986.; see icr.org/article/4473.

20. The field *intensity* (B) fluctuated up and down during and after the Flood, but the total field *energy* always decreased. For the technically minded, the energy is the volume integral of $B^2$.

21. Coe, R.S. and Prévot, M., Evidence suggesting extremely rapid field variation during a geomagnetic reversal, *Earth and Planetary Science* **92**(3/4):292–298, April 1989. See also the reports by Dr Andrew Snelling, *Creation* **13**(3):46–50; creation.com/magrev and **13**(4):44–48, 1991; creation.com/magage.

22. Coe, R.S., Prévot, M. and Camps, P., New evidence for extraordinarily rapid change of the geomagnetic field during a reversal, *Nature* **374**(6564):687–692, 1995; see also Snelling, A., The principle of 'least astonishment' *J. Creation* **9**(2):138–139, 1995; creation.com/magrev2.

23. Humphreys, D.R., The creation of planetary magnetic fields, *Creation Research Society Quarterly* **21**(3):140–149, 1984; creationresearch.org/crsq/articles/21/21_3/21_3.html

24. Hood, L.L., The enigma of lunar magnetism, *Eos* **62**(16):161–163, 1981.

25. The *Voyager* measurements were 3.0 and 1.5 × $10^{24}$ J/T for Uranus and Neptune respectively. Ness, N.F. *et al.*, Magnetic fields at Uranus, *Science* **233**(4759):85–89, 1986; Dessler, A.J., Does Uranus have a magnetic field? *Nature* **319**(6050):174–175, 1986; Kerr, R.A., The Neptune system in *Voyager*'s afterglow, *Science* **245**(4925):1450–1451, 1989.

26. Dr Humphreys had predicted field strengths of the order of $10^{24}$ J/T—*Creation Research Society Quarterly* **27**(1):15–17, 1990. The fields of Uranus and Neptune are hugely off-centred (0.3 and 0.4 of the planets' radii) and at a large angle from the planets' spin axis (60° and 50°). A big puzzle for dynamo theorists, but explainable by a catastrophe which seems to have affected the whole solar system (see Revelations in the solar system, creation.com/solarsystem).

27. Humphreys, D.R., Mercury's crust is magnetized: More good news for creation science, creation.com/mercury-magnetized-crust, 18 July 2012, and the 'Related articles' listed under the article. See also Chapter 3.

28. Magnetic moon findings support creationist's theory, *Creation* **19**(4):8, 1997; creation.com/focus-194#magmoons.

29. See Dr Humphreys' online article Beyond Neptune: Voyager II supports creation, ICR *Impact* # 203, May 1990, (archived at icr.org/article/329).

30. For example, in a simple electric circuit at time t with initial current I, resistance R and inductance L, the current is given by $i = Ie{-}t/\tau$, where $\tau$ is the time constant L/R—the time for the current to decay to 1/e (~37%) of its initial value. For a sphere of radius a, conductivity $\sigma$, and permeability $\mu$, $\tau$ is given by $\mu\sigma a^2/\pi^2$.

# Chapter 6

# Did life come to Earth from outer space?

Some evolutionists are now admitting that it's just impossible for life to have begun from non-living chemicals, on Earth. This is because every observation has confirmed the fact that here on Earth living things always only come from other living things by reproduction. Indeed, because there are no exceptions, this is known as the Law of Biogenesis, attributed to the French chemist Louis Pasteur. The term is from the Greek words *bios* (life) and *genesis* (birth, source or creation), and means that *living organisms are produced only by other living organisms*.

**Author: Russell Grigg[1]**

Nevertheless, the notion that life somehow originated on another planet and then came to Earth via outer space holds a wistful obsession for many evolutionists. This is because:

1. They have been unable to explain the origin of life on Earth, and even the 'simplest' living cell is now known to be unimaginably complex. So finding life in space could be used to promote the idea that it is inevitable for life to arise by itself from lifeless chemicals.

2. As life has been found deeper and deeper in the fossil record,[2] and so in older and older strata according to evolutionary dogma, many are now saying that there has not been enough time for life to have evolved on Earth; thus an older planet is needed.

3. Projects to investigate life elsewhere in the universe overshadow more mundane Earth-directed research in attracting public interest and tax dollars!

Of course, postulating that life began on another planet does not *solve* the evolutionists' problem of just how non-living chemicals could have turned into a living cell—it merely *transfers* it to another place.

## Wanted—a planet just like Earth!

### Conditions for life

The optimum place for life as we know it on Earth[3] to exist elsewhere in space would be a planet with features just like those of Earth. These include having a star very like our own sun (an exceptionally stable star—see Chapter 2), being in the 'habitable zone', i.e. the right distance from its sun,[4] as well as having an orbit[5] and speed of rotation[6] that would maintain a suitable temperature range, and hence fulfill the 'Goldilocks criterion'—not too hot, not too cold, just right.[7] Another essential would be the presence of liquid water—in living cells, water provides a liquid medium, necessary for amino acids and other organic molecules to mingle and react.[8]

Also needed would be an atmosphere that was non-poisonous,[9] and that would also absorb or deflect lethal doses of ultraviolet light, x-rays, and gamma rays, as

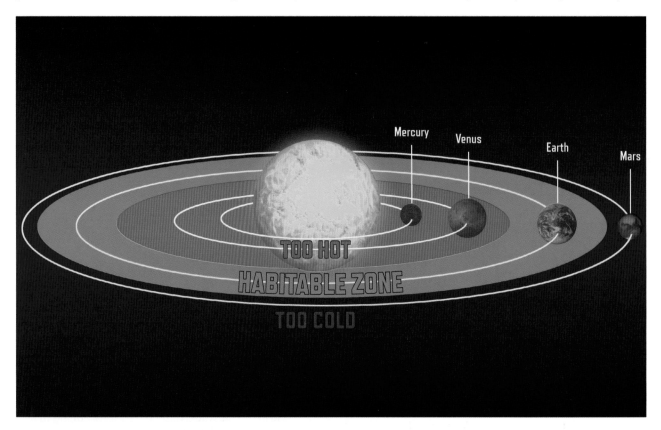

**Earth is the only planet in our solar system's Habitable Zone—not too hot, not too cold, just right for life to exist.**

**Water is essential for life. Earth is 71 per cent covered with it.**

well as a magnetic field strong enough to deflect the solar wind (a stream of high-energy charged particles from the sun which permeates the solar system).[10] Complex life forms would need oxygen to be present in the right proportion. Earth is just right for life.[11]

## Mars

Many researchers believe that Mars once fulfilled enough of these conditions for life to have existed there. However evidence of life has not been found, despite concerted efforts. Claims were made that a small (1.93 kg) 'Mars meteorite' designated ALH84001, which was picked up in Antarctica in 1984, contained fossilized micro-organisms, but those claims have been shown to be incorrect (see Chapter 9).[12,13] 'True believers' claimed that other meteorites said to have originated from Mars contained sulfur isotopes produced by bacteria, but analysis indicated the isotopes were produced by atmospheric chemical reactions.[14]

Several spacecraft sent to Mars malfunctioned or were lost, causing great disappointment, but the

**All the images of NASA's _Curiosity_ Rover on Mars show a very desolate Mars landscape. Researchers were hoping to find traces of life within the cold Martian soil, but none has been found.**

search for life on Mars continues, with the *Curiosity* rover arriving successfully on the surface of Mars on 6 August 2012.

Several lines of evidence suggest that Mars was once warm and wet and perhaps even suffered catastrophic flooding. However, all the many chemical and other tests of Martian rocks and soil have produced no evidence that life ever existed on Mars. Tests for indications of life have likewise failed elsewhere in the solar system, e.g. on Europa, one of Jupiter's moons, which may hold some liquid water, but has few, if any, of the other conditions necessary for life.

## Search for other planets

Astrobiology (the study of/search for extraterrestrial life) has been given a boost now that researchers have developed techniques for detecting exoplanets (or 'extrasolar' planets)—planets which orbit stars beyond our solar system. The two most successful techniques for detecting exoplanets are the Doppler method and the Transit method (see Chapter 16 for details).

## What has been found?

As of July 2016, using these and other methods, researchers have detected 3,371 confirmed exoplanets and 2,501 solar systems.[15] These have included many *multiplanetary* systems (stars with two or more confirmed planets), for example Upsilon Andromedae, about 44 light years from Earth,[16] and several *circumbinary* planets (planets that orbit two stars instead of one), for example Kepler-16b, orbiting the binary star Kepler-16. The nearest exoplanet to us is 4.37 light years away, orbiting the star Alpha Centauri B.

A few habitable zone exoplanets have been found, but most are much bigger than Earth. A handful of Earth-sized exoplanets have been found, but most have been in lethally-close orbits to their stars. As yet, no extrasolar planets have been found that fulfill all the conditions needed to support life (as outlined above), so the search continues.

## Further problems

Even if any extrasolar planets capable of supporting life do exist, several major factors would inhibit any rocks from those planets from carrying life to Earth. These are:

### 1. The need to achieve escape velocity

For a rock to break free from the pull of gravity of its mother planet, it must achieve a speed called the escape velocity. For Earth this is 11.186 km per second. Spacecraft usually require two or more stages of rocket propulsion to achieve this, with the secondary stages acting on the already speeding craft. For Mars escape velocity is 5.03 km per second. As volcanoes do not eject materials at these speeds, scientists postulate that rocks are blasted from planets and into space through giant asteroid collisions.

### 2. The tyranny of distance

The *nearest* star to Earth (beyond the sun) is Proxima Centauri. It is 4.3 light years away, which means that light—travelling at 300,000 km (186,000 miles) per second—takes 4.3 years to reach us, 40 million million km away. If an Earth-sized planet (the optimum size) were orbiting Proxima Centauri and a rock were blasted from it at the needed speed of Earth's escape velocity, the object would take well over 100,000 years to get here.[17] Any rock coming from an Earth-sized planet at the comparatively close distance of 40 light years away (or 1/2500th of the diameter of the Milky Way) would take over a million years to get here.

### 3. Other problems

"Radiation would destroy DNA on a journey between stars," says Francis Cucincotta of the NASA Johnson Space Centre in Houston.[18] Other hazards would be the near-absolute-zero temperature of space without a space suit, the lack of nutrients and/or oxygen in the vacuum of space without a space vehicle, entry into Earth's atmosphere without a heat shield, and impact with planet Earth without a parachute. Some idea of the force of such an impact was demonstrated by the catastrophic collision of a score of fragments of comet Shoemaker–Levy 9 with Jupiter on July 16–22, 1994 (see Chapter 10 for details).

All in all, interstellar space travel for living organisms is sheer wishful thinking.

## Biblical perspectives

There are no biblical or moral reasons why God should not have formed other planets, when He formed those in our own solar system on Day 4 of Creation Week

Copyright: phudui / 123RF Stock Photo

**SETI's Allen Telescope Array (ATA) in California has failed to find any evidence of intelligent life in outer space in over 50 years of sky-watching.**

(Genesis 1:14–19). Whether there is *life* on any planet other than Earth is another matter.

The Bible teaches that life began on Earth through creation by God (Genesis 1:11–27). It also tells us that God's purposes are centred on Earth. Thus God created Earth (on Day 1) before He created the "lights in the expanse of the heavens" (on Day 4), which were "to separate the day from the night" and were "for signs, and for seasons, and for days, and years" (Genesis 1:14), i.e. for the benefit of mankind.

Man and woman were both made "in the image of God" (Genesis 1:27). This, coupled with factors such as the Fall, the Incarnation, the Redemption of mankind through the once-only death and Resurrection of the Lord Jesus Christ, the Second Coming of Christ to Earth, and the coming Judgment of all mankind, shows Earth's unique importance among the billions and billions of stars in the universe. This is despite the frequent belittling, by evolutionists, of the importance of Earth.

The above also implies that God did not create life forms elsewhere in the universe, certainly not sentient life anyway.[19] If, however, some form of microbial life should one day be found on Mars, Europa, or elsewhere within our solar system, this would not prove that it had evolved (or been created) there. Such life could be seeded from Earth, because:

1. If rocks can be blasted from Mars to Earth, the process should also be possible from Earth to Mars, as physicist Paul Davies suggests.[20]
2. Bacterial spores may be able to survive the relatively short journey involved compared to interstellar travel.
3. Spores in Earth's upper atmosphere could be pushed into space and then to another planet or moon by the solar wind.
4. There is always the risk of contamination by Earth bacteria of a planet or moon on which any man-made space vehicle lands. This may already have happened on Mars (see Chapter 9).

Space-life enthusiasts like to say that 'absence of evidence is not evidence of absence'. Perhaps, but they have never been able to answer the celebrated question posed by Nobel-Prize-winning physicist Enrico Fermi half a century ago concerning all the other alleged civilizations in the universe: "Well then, where is everybody?" SETI, the Search for Extraterrestrial Intelligence, used equipment that could monitor 100 million channels simultaneously, but has failed to obtain a single 'intelligent' signal from outer space in over 50 years.

In April 2000, 600 astronomers, biologists, chemists, geologists, and other researchers met at the First Astrobiology Science Conference, held at NASA's Ames Research Centre, California,[21] to evaluate the evidence on whether, biologically speaking, we are alone in the universe. The predominant mood of pessimism was encapsulated by British paleontologist Simon Conway Morris's comment: "I don't think there is anything out there at all except ourselves," and Dan Cleese, a Mars program scientist at NASA's Pasadena Jet Propulsion Laboratory, who said that it is time to "tone down expectations".[22]

## Conclusion

The fervent search to authenticate 'astrobiology' has generated much data, but to date this has, if anything, strengthened the Genesis record of the creation of life on Earth by God. Contrary to the claims of evolutionists and the many imaginative Hollywood epics like *ET, Star Wars, Independence Day*, etc., the coming of aliens to Earth from outer space will always remain in the realm of science fiction.

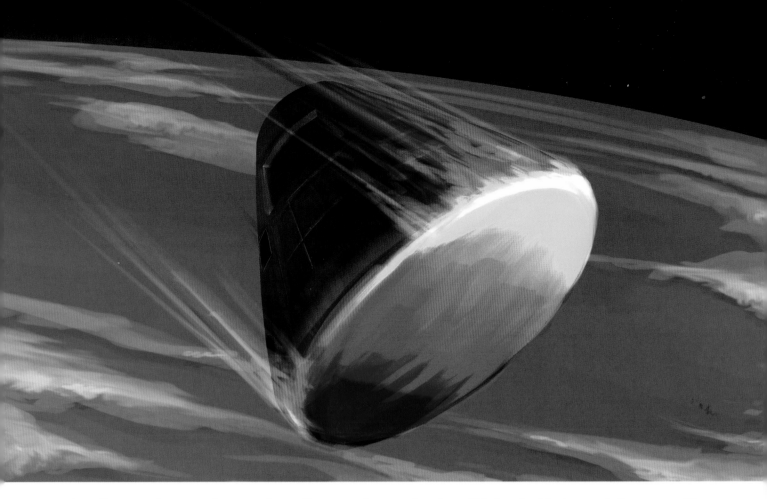

**A small spacecraft can use the atmosphere of its target planet to slow down. This 'aerobraking' converts the spacecraft's kinetic energy into heat, so a heatshield is needed to protect the module and any astronauts aboard. Shown is an artistic rendition of the *Apollo* Command Module re-entering Earth's atmosphere, after a lunar mission.**

# Feasibility of interstellar travel
## By Jonathan Sarfati

The following calculations are given for the benefit of the more technically minded.

**1.** For a spacecraft to acquire a speed of 1/10th the speed of light (c/10), the kinetic energy needed is given accurately enough by the non-relativistic formula of $\frac{1}{2}mv^2$. For a very small unmanned spacecraft of 10 kg, this is $\frac{1}{2} \times 10$ kg $\times (3 \times 10^7$ m/s$)^2 = 4.5 \times 10^{15}$ Joules. The largest hydroelectric power station in the world, Itaipu, jointly run by Brazil and Paraguay, has a huge output of 14 gigawatts (1 gigawatt = $10^9$ Joules per second ). It would take the total energy generated by the 20 turbines in 3.7 days to accelerate a 10 kg spacecraft to a speed of c/10, assuming perfect efficiency.

For a manned spacecraft weighing several tonnes, the energy requirements would greatly exceed the world's daily electricity consumption. For the city-sized spacecraft in the movie *Independence Day*, the energy requirements would be staggering. And when such a spacecraft slowed again using reverse thrust, it would need to use up almost this same amount of energy in braking. If the spacecraft had to accelerate to c/10, slow down and speed up many times, the energy needed would be many times greater. It would probably be impossible for enough fuel to be carried without some sort of antimatter drive.

If perfect annihilation—complete conversion of matter to energy ($E = mc^2$)—were possible, 1 tonne of antimatter could annihilate 1 tonne of ordinary matter to produce: 2000 kg $\times (3 \times 10^8$ m/s$)^2$, or $1.8 \times 10^{20}$ J. And this is the absolute maximum amount of energy that could be produced from a given mass of fuel. A real spacecraft could be nowhere near this efficient.

**2.** The kinetic energy of a speck of dust with a mass of just 0.1 gram impacting at c/10, calculated from the spacecraft's reference frame, is $\frac{1}{2}mv^2$, or $\frac{1}{2} \times 10^{-4}$ kg $\times (3 \times 10^7$ m/s$)^2 = 4.5 \times 10^{10}$ J. The combustion energy of TNT is 4520 kJ/kg, or $4.52 \times 10^9$ J/tonne. So $4.5 \times 10^{10}$ J is equivalent to 9.95 tonnes of TNT. Therefore the impact energy of a 0.1 g object hitting a spacecraft travelling at c/10 would be the equivalent to an explosion of about 10 tonnes of TNT.

Copyright: phudui / 123RF Stock Photo

**Movies like *Independence Day* have added to the public's fascination with the concept of life in outer space, however, any city-sized spacecraft is the ultimate in (non)-science fiction.**

## Conclusion

Many believe the supposition that, if intelligent life evolved on other planets millions of years ago, the beings would have had the time to develop the incredible technologies depicted in much sci-fi. However, no amount of advanced technology could actually defy or 'turn off' the laws of physics that govern our universe. This would be necessary even to travel close to the speed of light, let alone faster. These are insurmountable problems.

## References and Notes

1. This chapter adapted and updated from Grigg, R., *Creation* **22**(4):40–43, 2000; creation.com/did-life-come-from-outer-space.
2. E.g. the finding, in Western Australia, of fossilized microbes in rocks supposedly 3.5 billion years old. *Creation* **15**(4):9, 1993; Schopf, J.W., *Science* **260**(5108):640–646, 1993.
3. I.e. DNA-based. This rules out theoretical fantasies such as 'silicon-based life' and 'sulfur-based life'.
4. Earth's average distance from the sun is ~150 million km (93 million miles). At this distance, the energy received by Earth from the sun is just the right amount to maintain a temperature range on Earth mostly between 0° C and 40° C—the narrow limits required to sustain life. Some microbial organisms can tolerate lower or higher temperatures, but they are the exceptions, not the rule.
5. Earth's orbit around the sun is very nearly a perfect circle; if the orbit were an elongated ellipse with the sun at one focus, Earth's temperatures would be extremely high during closest approach and extremely low at the outer end of the orbit.
6. If Earth's speed of rotation were much slower, there would be extreme differences between day and night temperatures. If it were much faster, increased centrifugal forces would cause atmospheric gases to escape into space.
7. The inclination of the earth's axis of 23.44° provides seasons as Earth orbits the sun, and the length of our year means that these are of the right length to provide enough time for growing between sowing and reaping. Cf. a year only 88 days long as on Mercury, or 248 years long as on Pluto.
8. See Sarfati, J., The wonders of water, *Creation* **20**(1):44–47, 1997; see creation.com/water.
9. Carbon dioxide in large enough quantities is lethal to living organisms. On Earth it amounts to 0.04% of the atmosphere; on Mars it is 95.3%.
10. Earth has the right atmospheric density and magnetic field to achieve these objectives.
11. This section was adapted from Gitt, W., *Stars and their Purpose*, CLV, Bielefeld, Germany, pp. 141 ff., 2006.
12. See also Sarfati, J., Life from Mars? *J. Creation* **10**(3):293–296, 1996; creation.com/images/pdfs/tj/j10_3/j10_3_293-296.pdf.
13. Another blow to Mars 'life' claim, *Creation* **20**(2):8, March 1998, creation.com/focus-202#mars; Bradley, J.P., *et al.*, No 'nanofossils' in martian meteorite, *Nature* **390**(6659):454–456, 4 December 1997; Kerr, R.A., Putative martian microbes called microscopy artifacts, *Science* **278**(5344): 1706–1707, 5 December 1997.
14. Martians can vanish without leaving a trace, *New Scientist* **165**(2228):21, 4 March 2000.
15. NASA *PlanetQuest* website, planetquest.jpl.nasa.gov, accessed 29 July 2016.
16. Lissauer, J.J., Three planets for Upsilon Andromedae, *Nature* **398**(6729):659–660, 22 April 1999.
17. This shows that stories about manned space exploration to other stars (as well as inter-galactic warfare) are science fiction. See Gitt, W., God and the extra-terrestrials, *Creation* **19**(4):46–48, September 1997; creation.com/god&et. Also Chapter 7, Did God create life on other planets?
18. Martian gift, *New Scientist* **165**(2221):19, 15 January 2000.
19. We are not here discussing angelic or demonic life. Note that Romans 8:22 says that "the whole creation" was cursed as a result of Adam's rebellion. 2 Peter 3:12 speaks of the heavens being destroyed by fire, as the very elements dissolve in fiery heat, and Revelation 6:14 indicates that the cosmos will be rolled up like a scroll, before the restoration of all things. Werner Gitt writes: "[W]hy would a race of beings, not of Adam's (sinful) seed, have their part of creation affected by the Curse, and then be part of the restoration brought about by Christ, the last Adam? All of this would seem exceedingly strange." (Ref. 17). For those who speculate about Jesus dying on other worlds to redeem those from alien civilizations, note that the redeemed of Earth are spoken of as Christ's bride, for all eternity. Christ will not have multiple brides.
20. Interview on Radio 2GB, Sydney, Australia, 1 February 1996, reported in: Planets can swap rocks, *Creation* **18**(3):7, June 1996; creation.com/focus-183#rocks.
21. As a result of "NASA administrator Dan Goldin's desire to make the search for extraterrestrial life one of the central themes for his agency", Bortman, H. and Ball, P., Storming the Tower of Babel, *Nature* **404**(6779):700, 13 April 2000.
22. Boyd, R., "Sorry, but we are alone", *The Courier Mail*, Brisbane, Australia, 14 April 2000, p. 10.

# Chapter 7

# Did God create life on other planets?

## Otherwise why is the universe so big?

Many people, Christian or otherwise, struggle with the notion that the earth is the only inhabited planet in this enormous universe. Those who believe life evolved on the earth usually see it as virtual 'fact' that life has evolved on countless other planets. Discovering life on other planets would in turn be seen as confirming their evolutionary belief. Even many Christians think, "God must have created life elsewhere, otherwise this enormous universe would be an awful waste of space."

**Author: Gary Bates**[1]

In my experience, this seems to be the major underlying reason why people think that there must be other life 'out there'. However, our thinking should be based on what God has told us He did (the Bible), and not what we think He would, should or might have done.

### 'Big' is not a problem for God

Since Almighty God is the one who made the universe, it can scarcely be 'big' to Him. Humans struggle with its vastness because our comprehension is limited to the created time/space dimensions within which we exist, and it is mind-bending to try and comprehend anything beyond our dimensional existence. Size is only relative to us as inhabitants of this universe. And size and time are related somewhat. For example, because the universe is big to us, we consider how long it would take us to travel across it. But time itself began with the creation of the physical universe, so how can we comprehend what eternity is, or might be? Or what was 'before' the universe?

Similarly, how do we imagine how 'big' God is? We cannot use a tape measure that is made of the very atoms He made, to measure Him. One example of this might be if you were asked to build a small house and you did. Now you are asked to build a large house. In our dimensions, for you to build the larger house it would require more effort and take more time. So, is it harder, or does it take longer, for God to build a big universe compared to a smaller one (according to our perspective on what constitutes large or small)? Of course not, because God is not bound by either time or space (He is outside them both). Isaiah 40:28 says: "The Lord is the everlasting God, the Creator of the ends of the earth. He does not faint or grow weary … ."

We are impressed that God made billions of galaxies with billions of stars in them, and suitably so because that is one of the reasons He made them (Psalm 19:1). But as mentioned, size is not an issue for God. Stars are relatively simple structures as basically they are just great big balls of gas. It would take more 'creative input', in that sense, for Jesus' miracle of feeding the five thousand with the five loaves and two fish (Matthew 14:13–21) than for the creation of countless quasars (there is immense genetic complexity in the structure of even a dead fish).

**The Andromeda Galaxy is the nearest major galaxy to the Milky Way. It was no problem for God to create billions of galaxies any more than it was to create our solar system. He spoke—and they came into being.**

## The Bible and extraterrestrials (ETs)

It is often asked, "Just because the Bible teaches about God creating intelligent life only on Earth, why *couldn't* He have done so elsewhere?" After all, Scripture does not discuss everything, e.g. motorcars. However, the biblical objection to ET (extraterrestrial) life is not merely an argument from silence. Motorcars, for example, are not a salvation issue, but we believe that whether sentient, intelligent, moral-decision-capable beings (like us) exist elsewhere *is* such an issue, because this would undermine the authority of Scripture. In short, understanding the big picture of the Bible and its Gospel message allows us to conclude clearly that the reason the Bible doesn't mention extraterrestrials is because there aren't any.[2] Surely, if the earth were to be favoured with a visitation by real extraterrestrials from a galaxy far, far away, then one would reasonably expect that God in His sovereignty and foreknowledge would mention such a momentous

**We understand from the big picture of the Bible and its Gospel message that the reason the Bible doesn't mention ETs is because there aren't any.**

occasion in the Bible, because it would clearly redefine man's place in the universe.

1. The Bible indicates that the *whole creation* groans and travails under the weight of sin (Romans 8:18–22). The effect of the Curse following Adam's Fall was *universal*.[3] Otherwise what would be the point of God destroying this *whole creation* to make way for a new heavens and Earth—2 Peter 3:13, Revelation 21:1 ff? Therefore, any ETs living elsewhere would have been (unjustly) affected by the Adamic Curse through no fault of their own—they would not have inherited Adam's sin nature.

2. When Christ (God) appeared in the flesh, He came to Earth not only to redeem mankind but eventually the *whole creation* back to Himself (Romans 8:21, Colossians 1:20). However, Christ's atoning death at Calvary cannot save these hypothetical ETs, because one needs to be a physical descendant of Adam for Christ to be our "kinsman-redeemer" (Isaiah 59:20). Jesus was called "the last Adam" because there was a real first man, Adam (1 Corinthians 15:22, 45)—not a first Vulcan, Klingon, etc. This was so a sinless human Substitute could take on the punishment all humans deserve for sin (Isaiah 53:6,10; Matthew 20:28; 1 John 2:2, 4:10), with no need to atone for any (non-existent) sin of his own (Hebrews 7:27).

3. Since this would mean that any ETs would be lost for eternity when this present creation is destroyed in a fervent heat (2 Peter 3:10, 12), some have wondered whether Christ's sacrifice might be repeated elsewhere for other beings. However, Christ died *once for all* (Romans 6:10, 1 Peter 3:18) on *Earth*. He is not going to be crucified and resurrected again on other planets (Hebrews 9:26). This is confirmed by the fact that the redeemed (earthly) church is known as Christ's bride (Ephesians 5:22–33; Revelation 19:7–9) in a marriage that will last for eternity.[4] Christ is *not* going to be a polygamist with many other brides from other planets.

4. The Bible makes no provision for God to redeem any other species, any more than to redeem fallen angels (Hebrews 2:16).

**Earth is the only planet in our solar system that is favourable to life. Hence the search for extrasolar planets that may be similar to Earth. None has been found that fulfils all the necessary conditions for life.**

### Fitting them in there … somehow!

One attempt to fit ETs in the Bible is on the basis of a word in Hebrews 11:3: "Through faith we understand that the *worlds* were framed by the word of God, so that things which are seen were not made of things which do appear." (KJV)

The word 'worlds' appears in the KJV translation and some others, and some claim that it refers to other inhabitable planets. However, the Greek word is *aiōn* (*aiōn*), from which we derive the word 'eons'. Thus modern translations render the word as 'universe' (entire space-time continuum) because it correctly describes 'everything that exists in time and space, visible and invisible, present and eternal'. Even if it was referring to other planets, it is an unwarranted extrapolation to presume there is life on them of any sort, let alone *intelligent* life.

It should also be remembered that expressions like "the heavens and earth" (Genesis 1:1) are a figure of speech known as a *merism*. This occurs when two opposites or extremes are combined to represent the whole or the sum of its parts. For example, if I said "I painted the building from top to bottom", one would understand this to mean the whole building. Similarly, biblical Hebrew has no word for 'the universe' and can at best say 'the all', so instead it used the merism "the heavens and the earth". It is clear that New Testament passages like the aforementioned Romans 8:18–22 and Hebrews 11:3 are pointing back to the Genesis ('heavens and earth') creation, and thus, everything that God made, and when time as we know it began.

Another passage is John 10:16 in which Jesus says: "And I have other sheep that are not of this fold. I must bring them also, and they will listen to my voice. So there will be one flock, one shepherd." However, even an ET-believing astronomer at the Vatican (thus a 'hostile witness' to the 'no ETs cause'), a Jesuit priest by the name of Guy Consalmagno, concedes, "In context, these 'other sheep' are presumably a reference to the Gentiles, not extraterrestrials."[5] Jesus' teaching was causing division among the Jews (John 10:19), because they always believed that salvation from God was for them alone. Jesus was reaffirming that He would be the Saviour of *all* mankind.

### A novel approach

A more recent idea to allow for ETs arose out of a perceived need to protect Christianity in the event of a real alien visitation to Earth. Michael S. Heiser is an influential Christian UFOlogist/speaker with a Ph.D. in Hebrew Bible and Ancient Semitic Languages. He claims that the arguments put forward earlier might

**Rice terraces at Longsheng, Guangxi, China. Conditions that promote life on Earth include that our planet has liquid water, soil nutrients, a non-poisonous atmosphere, and protection from lethal solar radiation.**

not apply to God-created aliens. Because they are not descendants of Adam they have not inherited his sin nature, and thus, are not morally guilty before God. Just like 'bunny rabbits' on the earth, they do not need salvation—even though they will die, they are going to neither heaven nor hell.

On the surface this seems a compelling argument; after all, fallen angels are intelligent but are beyond salvation ("For surely it is not angels that he helps, but he helps the offspring of Abraham." Hebrews 2:16). Angels are immortal and not of our corporeal dimension. And Heiser's ETs in spaceships require a level of intelligence not found in rabbits. This acutely highlights the injustice of their suffering the effects of the Curse, including death and ultimately extinction when the heavens are 'rolled up like a scroll' (Revelation 6:14). It also seems bizarre to assign no moral responsibility for the actions of highly intelligent beings.

Heiser also claims that vastly intelligent ETs would not displace mankind's position as being made in the image of God because 'image' just means humans have been placed as God's representatives on the earth.

However, the Bible says we are made in God's image *and likeness* (Genesis 1:26). Man was immediately created a fully intelligent being about 6,000 years ago and was involved in craftsmanship shortly thereafter (Genesis 4:22). Since that time, even we have not been able to develop technologies advanced enough to travel to other star systems. If aliens were capable of developing incredible faster-than-light spaceships needed to get here, one would presume they must have been created with vastly superior intellect to ours—which would make them even more in God's likeness in that sense than we are. Or, their creation is much older than the 6,000 years of the biblical six-day timeframe; the aliens were created before man and had sufficient time to develop their technologies. However, God created Earth on Day 1 and later the heavenly bodies on Day 4.

## Influenced from outside the Bible

Although Heiser does not promote theistic evolution, he is sympathetic to a universe billions of years old, as proposed by the progressive creationist Dr Hugh Ross,[6] and rejects biblical inerranccy. In theory, this could allow the time necessary for any unseen ETs to develop the almost science-fiction-like technologies required to get here. But, this is circular reasoning.

There is a huge problem for the Gospel in these long ages. First, it's important to understand that the modern scientific idea of long ages (i.e. millions and billions of years) is derived from the *belief* that sedimentary rock layers on Earth represent eons of time.[7] This in turn is derived from the dogmatic *assumption* that there were no special acts of creation or a global Flood, so that Earth's features must be explained by processes seen to be happening now.[8] This philosophy of *uniformitarianism* seems to amply fulfil the Apostle Peter's prophecy recorded in 2 Peter 3:3–7.

The conflict with the Gospel is that these very same rock layers contain fossils—a record of dead things showing evidence of violence, disease, and suffering. Thus, taking a millions-of-years view, even without evolution, places death and suffering long before the Fall of Adam. This undermines the Gospel and the very reasons that Christ came to the earth—such as reversing the effects of the Curse. Romans 5:12 clearly states that sin and death entered into the creation as a result of Adam's actions. There was no death before the Fall.

### Ranking the created order

Psalm 8:5 says that man was made a little lower than the angels and crowned with glory and honour. Heiser has said that salvation is based upon ranking, not intelligence. If so, where in the Bible (which omits to mention them) would ETs sit in this pecking order? Would they be higher than man, and lower than angels, for example?

If these advanced ETs were capable of visiting the earth, mankind would now be subject to *their* dominion. (Even if the ETs were friendly, potentially they would be much more powerful due to their intelligence and technology.) This would be in direct contravention to God's ordained authority structure when He ordered mankind to 'subdue' the earth—also known as the dominion mandate (Genesis 1:28).

### Be 'awe' inspired

Psalm 19:1 tells us a major reason that the universe is so vast: "The heavens declare the glory of God; and the sky above proclaims His handiwork." There are many similar passages in Scripture. They help us understand who God is and how powerful He is.

It reminds us that the more we discover about this incredible universe, the more we should be in awe of the One who made it all. In short, rather than looking up and thinking 'I wonder what else is out there?' and imagining aliens we've never seen, we should instead be considering the very One who made it.

**Grand Canyon provides evidence of rapid catastrophic processes. The horizontal strata indicate the layers were laid down with high energy over an enormous geographical area, and the straight contacts indicate there was no time for erosion between one layer and the next.**

## Could there be 'simple life' elsewhere in space?

The Bible's 'big picture' seems to preclude *intelligent* life elsewhere in God's universe (see main text). But what if bacteria were found on other planets, for example? This is exceedingly unlikely, but 'God-made' bacteria would not violate the Gospel.[9] And in any case, any 'microbes on Mars' would most likely be the result of human contamination.[10]

In fact, *Nature* reports that swabs of the surface of the *Curiosity* rover to Mars before it was launched revealed that 65 species of bacteria survived inadequate sterilization procedures. Most were related to the genus *Bacillus*. Scientists laboratory-tested these microbes by desiccation (drying), UV exposure, cold, and pH extremes (acidity/alkalinity), and nearly 11% of the 377 strains survived more than one of these severe conditions.[11] So these hardy hitchhikers left Earth; whether or not they survived arrival on Mars remains to be seen, although 29 percent of the bacteria were able to metabolize perchlorate and sulphate, chemicals naturally present on Mars. And John Grunsfeld, Associate Administrator for the Science

***Nature* ran this NASA picture with the following heading: "Microbial stowaways to Mars identified: Bacteria found on *Curiosity* rover reveal the types of microorganisms that spacecraft carry."**

Mission Directorate, quipped at a news conference: "We know there's life on Mars already because we sent it there."[12]

If bacteria are found elsewhere in the solar system, whether on Mars or anywhere else, it will be hailed as proof that life can 'just evolve'.[13] However, we have previously predicted in print that in such an unlikely event, the organisms will have earth-type DNA, etc., consistent with having originated from here as contaminants—either carried by recent man-made probes, or riding fragments of rock blasted from Earth by meteorite impacts.

The entire focus of creation is mankind on this Earth; the living forms on Earth's beautifully balanced biosphere are part of our created life support system.

### References and Notes

1. This chapter adapted and updated from Bates, G., *Creation* **29**(2):12–15, 2007; creation.com/did-god-create-life-on-other-planets. Gary Bates is also author of *Alien Intrusion: UFOs and the evolution connection*, Creation Book Publishers, Powder Springs, Georgia, USA, 2011.
2. Of course, there are angelic beings. These were made early in Creation Week—referred to as 'sons of God' and 'morning stars' in the poetry of the book of Job, they rejoiced and sang at the formation of the earth's 'foundations' (Job 38:7).
3. Sarfati, J., The Fall: a cosmic catastrophe: Hugh Ross's blunders on plant death in the Bible, *J. Creation* **19**(3):60–64, 2005; creation.com/plant_death.
4. The church was bought with the blood of its Saviour from the wound in His side, a clear analogy to the first woman being born from a 'wound' in Adam's side.
5. Consolgmagno, G., Humans are not God's only intelligent works, 3 January 2006. He actually took the affirmative side in a debate with CMI's Dr Jonathan Sarfati. They didn't see each other's arguments before publication in the liberal *Science and Theology News*. Both sides are now available although without author bylines at beliefnet.com.
6. Ross believes in soulless man-like creatures before Adam, similar in spiritual status to Heiser's hypothetical ETs. For a complete refutation of Ross's ideas see *Refuting Compromise* by Jonathan Sarfati, Master Books, Arkansas, USA, 2011.
7. Henry, J.F., An old age for the earth is the heart of evolution, *Creation Research Society Quarterly* **40**(3):164–172, December 2003.
8. Mortenson, T., *The Great Turning Point*, Master Books, Arkansas, USA, 2004.
9. See creation.com/is-the-bible-falsifiable.
10. See Chapter 9, Mars, the red planet.
11. Madhusoodanan, J., Microbial stowaways to Mars identified, *Nature* News, 19 May 2014. See also Smith, S. *et al*, American Society for Microbiology, 114th Annual Meeting, 17–20 May 2014, Boston, Massachusetts.
12. Quoted in *The Washington Post*, 28 Sept. 2015; *The New Yorker* 8 Oct. 2015; *Phys Org*, 29 Oct. 2015; and other publications.
13. Matthews, M., Space life? Answering unearthly allegations, *Creation* **25**(3):54–55, 2003; creation.com/space_life.

# Chapter 8

# The Moon: the light that rules the night

God created it. Man reached it. Poets have written about it. Here are some fascinating truths behind our great 'lesser light'. The moon has been an object of wonder since the dawn of mankind. It lights up the night sky like nothing else in the heavens, and indeed that is one of its purposes. It also causes tides to ebb and flow on Earth. This keeps our oceans from stagnating, which promotes fish life, as well as daily cleansing the shores of the lands we live on. The moon is well designed for our life on Earth, while its origin baffles evolutionists.

**Author: Jonathan Sarfati**

## The moon's origin

Although there are many different ideas on how and when the moon formed, no scientist was there at the time. So we should rely on the witness of One who *was* there (cf. Job 38:4), and who has revealed the truth in Genesis 1:14–19:

> "And God said, 'Let there be lights in the expanse of the heavens to separate the day from the night. And let them be for signs and for seasons, and for days and years, and let them be lights in the expanse of the heavens to give light upon the earth.' And it was so. And God made the two great lights—the greater light to rule the day and the lesser light to rule the night—and the stars. … And

there was evening and there was morning, the fourth day."

This passage clearly states that God made the moon on the same day that He made the sun and stars—the fourth day of Creation Week. It was also created one day after God created the plants. This order of events is impossible to reconcile with evolutionary/billions-of-years ideas.

## What is the moon's purpose?

The answer is in Genesis! A major purpose is to light up the night. The moon reflects the sun's light back to us even when the sun is on the other side of the earth. The amount of reflected light depends on the moon's surface area, so we are fortunate to have a moon that is so large. It is over a quarter of Earth's diameter—far larger in comparison with its planet than other moon-planet combinations in the solar system (apart from Charon and its dwarf planet Pluto). If it were much smaller, it would not have enough gravity to maintain its spherical shape.[2]

Another purpose for the moon is to show the seasons. The moon orbits the earth roughly once a month, causing regular phases in a 29½ day cycle (see diagram). This meant calendars could be made, and people could plant their crops at the best time of the

**The moon is over one-quarter the diameter of Earth. This gives us enough, but not too much, moonlight at night.**

**Phases of the moon, as seen looking southward from the northern hemisphere.**

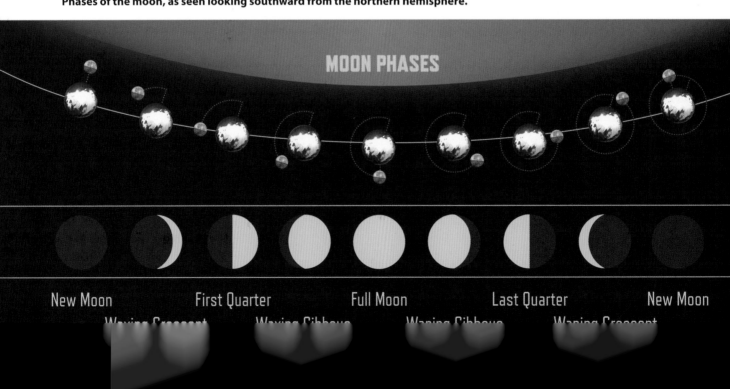

MOON PHASES

New Moon            First Quarter            Full Moon            Last Quarter            New Moon

Waxing Crescent      Waxing Gibbous      Waning Gibbous      Waning Crescent year. The moon's gravity exerts a stabilizing effect on the earth's tilt, maintaining the seasons. And another significant feature is that the moon always keeps the same face towards the earth.[3]

## Tides

The earth's gravity keeps the moon in orbit, and is so strong that it would need a steel cable 850 km (530 miles) in diameter to provide an equivalent binding force without breaking. The moon exerts the same force on the earth.[4] But the force is somewhat higher on the part of the earth nearest the moon, so any water there will bulge towards it, resulting in a high tide. The part furthest from the moon is attracted the least by the moon, so flows away from the moon (and Earth's centre), producing another high tide on the opposite side of the earth. In between, the water level must drop—causing low tides. As the moon orbits the spinning earth, there is a cycle of two high tides and two low tides about every 25 hours.

Tides are vital to life on Earth. They cleanse the ocean's shorelines, and help keep the ocean currents circulating, preventing the ocean from stagnating, thus allowing fish and other creatures to live there. Tides also benefit man by scouring out shipping channels and diluting sewage discharges. In some places, people exploit the energy of the tides to generate electricity.[5] The moon is at just the right distance for all of this—much farther away and tides would be too small; much closer and tides would be harmful to us.

## Nice to visit, but to live ... ?

One of the most dramatic events of our time was the landing of men on the moon. The first manned mission was USA's *Apollo 11*, which touched down on July 20, 1969. Since then there have been a further five manned US landings, as well as numerous unmanned missions by the Soviet Union, USA, India, China, and the European Space Agency.

The Apollo astronauts confirmed that the moon is a lifeless, airless world, with huge temperature extremes, and no liquid water. From the moon, Earth appears as a bright blue-and-white object in the black

**The lunar module from *Apollo 17* on the moon. Notice how inhospitable to life the landscape is.**

sky. Earth is the planet God has designed for life. Man may be able to live on other worlds one day, but it will be a forbidding task to make them habitable.

Many people don't realise that the man behind the Apollo moon mission was the creationist rocket scientist Wernher von Braun.[6] And another creationist, Jules Poirier, designed some vital navigational equipment used in the space program.[7]

### How long has the moon been receding?

Friction by the tides is slowing the earth's rotation, so the length of a day is increasing by 0.0017 seconds per century. This means that the earth is losing *angular momentum*.[8] The *Law of Conservation of Angular Momentum* says that the angular momentum the earth loses must be gained by the moon. Thus the moon is slowly receding from Earth at 3.8 cm (1½ inches) per year, and the rate would have been greater in the past.

The moon could never have been closer than 18,400 km (11,450 miles), known as the *Roche Limit* (after French astronomer Édouard Roche, 1821–1883), because Earth's gravity would then have been greater than the moon's gravitational self-attraction and so would have shattered it.

**This is the ascent stage of the *Apollo 11* Lunar Module, with Neil Armstrong and Buzz Aldrin aboard, on its way back up to the moon-orbiting Command Module, where Michael Collins took this photo of the ascending spacecraft and moon surface, with Earth in the far distance.**

But even if the moon had started receding from being in contact with the earth, it would have taken only 1.37 billion years to reach its present distance.[9] Note: this is the *maximum* possible age—far too young for evolution (and much younger than the radiometric 'dates' assigned to moon rocks)—it is not the actual age.

Obviously the moon cannot have been orbiting Earth for 4 billion years, as evolutionists claim.

### Could the moon have formed itself?

Evolutionists (and progressive creationists) deny the moon's direct creation by God. They have come up with several theories (below), but these all have serious holes, as many evolutionists themselves admit. For example, lunar researcher S. Ross Taylor said: "The best models of lunar origin are the testable ones, but the testable models for lunar origin are wrong."[10] Another astronomer said, half-jokingly, that there were no good (naturalistic) explanations, so the best explanation was observational error—the moon does not exist![11]

1. *Fission theory*, invented by the astronomer George Darwin (son of Charles). He proposed that the earth spun so fast that a chunk broke off and formed the moon. But this theory is universally discarded today. The earth could never have spun fast enough to throw a moon into orbit, and the escaping moon would have been shattered while within the Roche Limit.

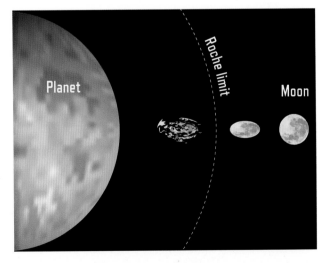

**Moons are held together by their own gravity. If one approaches too close to a planet, it will disintegrate where the planet's gravitational pull is greater than the self-attraction of the moon. This distance from the centre of the planet is called the Roche limit.**

2. *Capture theory*—the moon was wandering through the solar system, and was captured by Earth's gravity. But the chance of two bodies passing close enough is minute. Also, in such a scenario, the moon would have been accelerated by Earth's gravity as it approached and by the time it arrived would have been going too fast to stay in orbit, so it would either have hit the earth or been 'slingshotted' like an artificial satellite into space. Finally, a capture would have resulted in an elongated comet-like orbit.

3. *Condensation* or *nebular theory*—the moon grew out of a dust cloud attracted by Earth's gravity. However, no such cloud could be dense enough, and it doesn't account for the moon's low iron content, i.e. moon rocks brought back by the *Apollo* missions proved to be different from Earth rocks.

4. *Impact theory*—the currently fashionable idea that material was blasted off from Earth by the impact of another planetary body. This hypothetical object has even been given names—Theia (a mythical Greek goddess); it is also sometimes called Orpheus. Again, the chance of two objects impacting is minute, as per the 'Capture theory'. And calculations show

that to get enough material to form the moon, the impacting object would need to have been twice as massive as Mars. Then there is the unsolved problem of losing the excess angular momentum.[12] Finally, some of the moon rocks brought back to Earth have been found to contain water, but this is contrary to the Impact theory because any water would have been vapourised and lost during the collision.

## What about the moon's craters?

The explanation for lots of craters on the moon is a brief intense swarm of meteoroids, travelling on parallel paths, probably during the Flood year. This is supported by ghost craters, evidence of rapid succession of impacts, and by the fact that 11 of the 12 maria (plains areas) are in one quadrant, evidence that the major impacts occurred before the moon had moved far enough in one orbit (month) to show a different face to the swarm[13,14]

Ghost craters on the moon's maria are a problem for long ages. Enormous impacts apparently caused the lava flows, but not before other, smaller, impact craters formed within the larger craters. These can be seen as 'ghosts' under the lava flows. But this means that the smaller impacts can't have been very long after the huge

**This massive moon boulder dwarfs *Apollo 17*'s astronaut Harrison H. Schmitt and his Lunar Roving Vehicle. The moon's utter barrenness should remind us of planet Earth's unique design for life.**

**Ghost craters on the moon (arrowed) are the faint circular rims of craters that have been covered by molten rock. They were formed by meteor impacts that have been partially filled with lava.**

ones, otherwise the lava would have hardened before the impacts. So it was a very short time frame for the cratering. This also implies that other cratered bodies of our solar system are also much younger than assumed.[15]

Maria are largely absent on the heavily cratered far side of the moon. This is out of view from Earth, but has been photographed from spacecraft in lunar orbit. The likely explanation is that the crust there is too thick for impact to cause these lava flows.

## Reflectivity or albedo of the moon

The degree to which planets and moons reflect their sun's light is called their albedo (from Latin *albus* = white). The Bond albedo, named after the American astronomer George P. Bond (1825–1865), refers to the fraction of the total energy impinging on an astronomical surface that is scattered back into space in all directions. The geometric albedo is the fraction reflected as seen from the light/energy source, i.e. back along the direction of illumination. Both are given as a number between 0 and 1, with 1 = 100 per cent.

NASA gives the moon's Bond albedo as 0.11, and its visual geometric albedo as 0.12, i.e. 11% and 12% respectively.

# Moon Facts[1]

| | |
|---|---|
| Average distance from Earth | 378,000 km (234,880 miles) |
| Mass | 0.07346 × 10²⁴ kg (1.23% Earth) |
| Equatorial radius | 1738.1 km (27.25% Earth) |
| Volume | 2.1968 × 10¹⁰ km³ (2.03% Earth) |
| Mean density | 3344 kg/m³ (60.6% Earth) |
| Surface gravity | 1.62 m/s² (16.5% Earth) |
| Escape velocity | 2.38 km/sec (21.3% Earth) |
| Sidereal rotation period[2] | 655.728 hours (27.322 Earth days) |
| Synodic period[2] | 29.53 Earth days |
| Surface temperature range | 117° C (243° F) day, -178° C (-288° F) night |
| Recession rate from Earth | 3.8 cm/yr |

1. Source: NASA Moon Fact Sheet updated 19 April 2016.
2. The sidereal rotation period is the time for a complete orbit of the moon around the earth, relative to an observer outside the solar system. The phase cycle (synodic period) is the time taken for the moon to return to the same orientation towards the sun. This is longer because the earth moves about 1/13th of the way in its orbit around the sun, so the moon must travel further than one true lunar orbit for a given orientation to recur.

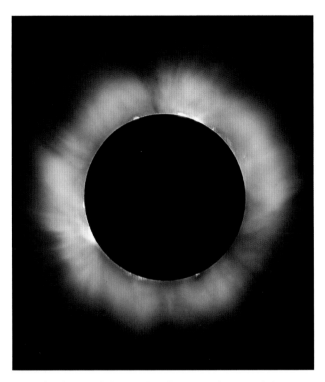

**A total eclipse of the sun by the moon is one of the most spectacular events in the daytime sky.**

## When day becomes night …

One of the most fascinating sights in the sky is a total eclipse of the sun. This is possible because the moon is almost exactly the same angular size (half a degree) in the sky as the sun—it is both 400 times smaller and 400 times closer than the sun. This looks like design. If the moon had really been receding for billions of years, and man had been around for a tiny fraction of that time, the chances of mankind living at a time so we could observe this precise size matchup would be remote. See also Eclipse, Chapter 2.

## Conclusion

The moon is a good example of the heavens declaring God's glory (Psalm 19:1). It does what it's designed to do, and it is vital for life on Earth. It is also a headache for evolutionists/uniformitarians.

## References and Notes

1. This chapter adapted and updated from Sarfati, J., *Creation* **20**(4):36–39, 1998; creation.com/the-moon-the-light-that-rules-the-night.
2. The most stable shape for a massive body is for all parts of the surface to be the same distance from the centre of mass, i.e. a sphere. The pressure inside the moon is ten times the crushing strength of granite, so any large unevenness would be crushed into shape. Such a sphere may bulge at the equator if the body is spinning fast enough.
3. That is, its rotational period is identical to its (synodic or solar) orbital period. This is true of many moons in the solar system, because the planet's gravity is always stronger on the nearest side (a tidal interaction), and this will eventually lock one side so it will always face the planet. The effect is enhanced if one side is denser than the other.
4. Gravitational force between two objects is given by $F = Gm_1m_2/R^2$, where G is the gravitational constant, $m_1$ and $m_2$ are the masses of the objects, and R is the distance between their centres of mass—an *inverse square law*. But the tidal effect drops off far more quickly, with $R^3$—an inverse *cube* law. If more people had known this, they wouldn't have been scared by knowing all the planets would be roughly aligned in 1982, when many predicted this would lead to disaster. See also Planet alignment disasters? *Creation* **34**(1):53, 2012; creation.com/comet-elenin#planet.
5. Fred Pearce, Catching the tide, *New Scientist* **158**(2139):38–41, 20 June 1998.
6. See Ann Lamont, *21 Great Scientists who Believed the Bible*, Creation Science Foundation, Australia, 1995, pp. 242–251. Also *Creation* **16**(2):26–30, 1994.
7. For more details, see Jules H. Poirier: Specialist design engineer (aeronautics and electronics); see creation.com/jules-h-poirier.
8. Angular momentum = mvr, the product of mass, velocity and distance, and is always conserved (constant) in an isolated system.
9. For the technical reader: since tidal forces are inversely proportional to the cube of the distance, the recession rate (dR/dt) is inversely proportional to the *sixth power* of the distance. So $dR/dt = k/R^6$, where k is a constant = (present speed: 0.04 m/year) × (present distance: 384,404,000 m)$^6$ = 1.29 × 10$^{50}$ m$^7$/year. Integrating this differential equation gives the time to move from Ri to Rf as $t = \frac{1}{7}k (Rf^7 - Ri^7)$. For Rf = the present distance and Ri = the Roche Limit, t = 1.37 × 10$^9$ years. There is no significant difference if Ri = 0, i.e. the earth and moon touching, because of the high recession rate (caused by enormous tides) if the moon is close. See also Henry, J., The moon's recession and age, *J. Creation* **20**(2):65–70, August 2006; creation.com/moon-age.
10. S. Ross Taylor, paraphrased by geophysicist Sean Solomon, at Kona, Hawaii, Conference on Lunar Origin, 1984, cited in Hartmann, Wm. K., *The History of Earth*, p. 44, Workman Publishing Co., Inc., Broadway, NY, 1991.
11. Irwin Shapiro in a university astronomy class about 20 years ago, cited by J.J. Lissauer, Ref. 12, p. 327. Lissauer affirms that the first three theories have insoluble problems.
12. Shigeru Ida, *et al.*, Lunar accretion from an impact generated disk, *Nature* **389**(6649):353–357, 25 September 1997; Comment in the same issue by J.J. Lissauer, It's not easy to make the moon, pp. 327–328. See also J. Henry, Ref. 9.
13. Samec, G. On the origin of lunar maria, *J. Creation* **22**(3):101–106, Dec. 2008; creation.com/lunar/maria.
14. Faulkner, D., A biblically based cratering theory, *J. Creation* **13**(1):100–1045, April 1999; creation.com/a-biblically-based-cratering-theory.
15. Walker, T., and Catchpoole, D., Lunar volcanoes rock long-age timeframe, *Creation* **31**(3):18, 2009; creation.com/lunar-volcanoes-rock-long-age-timeframe.

# Chapter 9

# Mars: the red planet

Mars is the famous 'red planet', and is named after the Roman god of war. The fourth planet from the sun, it can approach the third planet, Earth, as closely as 54.6 million kilometres (33.9 million miles). Of course, this is still a huge distance, so it's only recently that a number of probes have been sent there. Being so close to us makes Mars one of the brightest objects in the night sky, surpassed only by our moon, Venus, and sometimes Jupiter.

Many hope that Mars is hospitable to life.

**Author: Jonathan Sarfati[1]**

This hope has not been realized, and is not likely to be. Mars is a dry, frigid world—yet recent discoveries point to huge floods in the past.

## What is Mars like?

Mars is only about half the diameter of Earth, and one-tenth the mass. In fact, it is roughly intermediate in size between Earth and our moon. Mars itself has two moons, named Phobos (fear) and Deimos (panic), after the horses that pulled the chariot of the Greek war god Ares, the counterpart of the Roman war god Mars. They are much tinier than our moon and orbit much closer to their planet. Phobos is only 26 km × 16 km, and orbits just over 6,000 km from Mars, Deimos is even smaller at 16 km × 10 km, but orbits over 23,000 km away. Because they are so small they are irregularly shaped—because they lack sufficient gravity to compress either of them into a more spherical shape.

Mars has the distinction of having the largest volcano in the solar system: Olympus Mons, 27 km high—three times the elevation of Mount

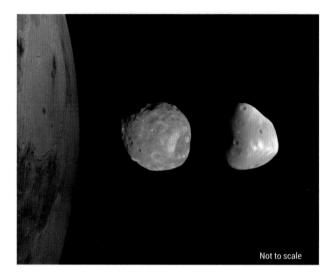

Not to scale

**Mars has two non-spherical moons, which always present the same face to their planet, i.e. they are tidally locked to Mars.**

Everest. Being a shallow-sloping shield volcano, it is enormously wide, 550 km (340 miles). In fact, Mt Everest could fit in its crater! Mars also has the largest canyon in the solar system. Called Valles Marineris,

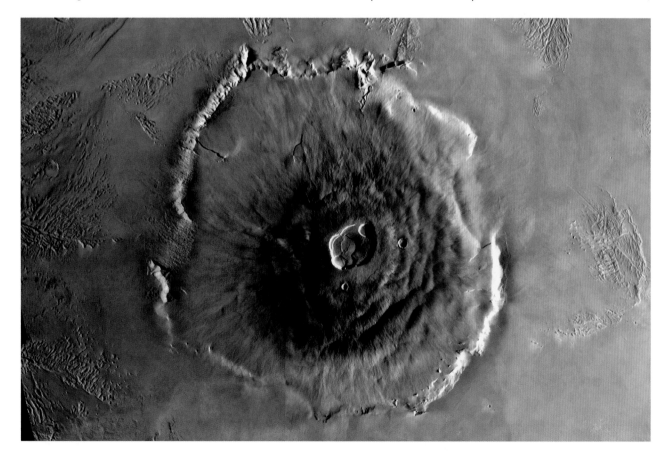

**Olympus Mons (Mount Olympus) is the largest volcano in the solar system. It is located just below the Mars' equator.**

it is more than 9 times as long as the Grand Canyon, about 7 times as wide, and 4 times as deep—that's almost as deep as Mt Everest is high.

Mars is nowhere near as hospitable as Earth. Its atmosphere is 100 times thinner than ours and comprises about 95% carbon dioxide. And while Mars is only 50% farther from the sun than Earth, that's enough to cause temperatures well below freezing most of the time, and thus to preclude the possibility of liquid water. Conversely, Earth's orbit, as well as its size, are well designed for life.

Mars' famous redness has nothing to do with heat, but is caused by ferric (iron) oxide, basically *rust*. Mars has polar ice caps, which grow and shrink visibly over the seasons. But they consist mainly of dry ice, i.e. solid carbon dioxide.

## Mars' origin according to an eyewitness

For the truth about the origin of anything, it helps to have a reliable eyewitness record. Such a record always outweighs any circumstantial evidence that might be interpreted in another way. Genesis claims to be a witness of One who was there—the Creator. Genesis 1:16–19:

> "And God made two great lights; the greater light to rule the day, and the lesser light to rule the night: he made the stars also … . And the evening and the morning were the fourth day."

The Hebrew word for 'stars' refers to any bright object in the sky, so includes the planets of our solar system, and by extension, any planets around other stars.[2] (See also Chapter 16.) So Mars was created on Day 4 of Creation Week, three days after Earth, about 6,000 years ago.[3]

## Life on Mars?

This cold, dry, rusty planet has been the subject of the most famous 'alien invasion' story of all time, *The War of the Worlds*, by evolutionist and eugenicist[4] Herbert George Wells (1866–1946). A USA radio broadcast on 30 October 1938 by famous actor and producer Orson Welles (1915–1985) caused widespread panic as many people mistook fiction for fact.

It's no accident that evolutionists like Wells liked the idea—after all, if life evolved on Earth, then surely it must have evolved elsewhere. Such ideas still greatly motivate searches for extra-terrestrial life.[5]

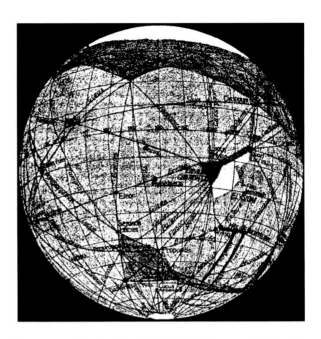

Astronomer Percival Lovell (1855–1916) promoted the view that there were canals on Mars with imaginative drawings such as this. Various NASA and other missions to Mars have shown the markings to be an optical illusion.

## Canals?

Much of this hope sprang from astronomer Giovanni Schiaparelli (1835-1910), who claimed that he had found long straight lines on Mars that he called *canali*. This is actually Italian for 'channels', but was mistranslated 'canals', yet he didn't rule out that they might be artificial. This inspired American businessman and astronomer Percival Lowell (1855-1916) to study Mars extensively, and he speculated that the 'canals' were built by an intelligent civilization to tap the polar icecaps, which he thought were the last source of water for a dying world. However, Vincenzo Cerulli (1859-1927) showed that these canals/channels didn't even exist, but were an optical illusion. Similarly, a much-touted giant 'face' on Mars (in 1976) was conclusively proven to be an illusion from shadows of an ordinary land mass.[6]

## Missions to Mars[7]

Nevertheless, a number of missions were sent to Mars, largely to find life. The first to probe the surface were the two *Viking* spacecraft, landing in 1976. They were equipped with advanced miniature chemical laboratories to analyze the Martian soil. But to much secular disappointment, they found not the slightest

*Above:* The NASA *Curiosity* rover examines a rock on Mars with a set of tools at the end of the rover's arm, which extends about 2 metres. Note how inhospitable to life the Mars surface is.

*Below:* The *Atlas V* rocket launch of NASA's *Curiosity* spacecraft on 26 Nov. 2011. Up until mid-2016 there have been some 53 (variously successful) missions to Mars by the USA, Soviet Union, Japan, European Union, Russia, China, and India. Another seven missions are planned to 2020, with United Arab Emirates joining in, and Mars' moons are attracting more proposed events.

trace of life. Some hopes came from certain reactions in the soil, but most scientists regard them as the result of super-oxidizing chemicals, which would actually destroy life.

In 2004, two probes landed on Mars: *Spirit*, active until 2010; and *Opportunity*, still sending data in 2016. In 2008, the *Phoenix* mission made the first successful landing at the poles. This found perchlorate ($ClO_4^-$), a very powerful oxidizer, which would destroy life.

In 2012, the *Curiosity* rover landed, and its onboard soil lab detected methane. Some evolutionists speculated that this could have a biological origin, because some organisms on Earth produce this gas. But they also realize that methane can have an inorganic origin[8]—e.g. there is abundant methane on the gas giants, and this certainly has no biological origin. There is also a logical inconsistency about the former explanation: finding a simple molecule like methane supposedly proves a complex origin from living creatures, but finding a living creature would supposedly prove that it evolved from simple chemicals.

Another irony is that *Curiosity* was not properly sterilized, mainly because they underestimated bacterial resilience in face of extreme conditions. So probably about 65 species of bacteria, mainly in the genus *Bacillus*, might have made it to Mars. Furthermore, a third of them could metabolize

**This is the rock found in Antarctica that was claimed to be a meteorite from Mars. The cube shows dimensions of 1 cm.**

perchlorate, so might have given a false positive for living processes. That is, it would be evidence of life on Mars, but only because it was sent from Earth in the first place.[9]

## Meteorite with life from Mars?

In 1996, around the time the movie *Independence Day* was launched, NASA made huge headlines with claims that a 1.93-kg meteorite from Mars, ALH84001 (found in 1984 in Alan Hills, Antarctica), had remains of living cells. The atheists and humanist groups of course made much of it. But immediately CMI pointed out[10] that the alleged evidence was very doubtful, e.g. chemicals like PAHs (polycyclic aromatic hydrocarbons) and magnetite crystals have been shown to form from non-living processes. We showed that there was much evidence against the claim, such as the wrong isotope ratios, and the fact that the alleged structures were far too small to hold enough DNA to store the minimal information required for life.[11]

Our stance has stood the test of time,[12] while the extravagant claims were quietly dropped, although there have been tentative revivals from time to time. But this is typical of much evolutionary propaganda. It's announced with front-page fanfare, but later downplaying or even retraction receives little publicity, if any.

## Floods on Mars?

Mars has frozen water at the poles; however there is no liquid water on Mars now. In fact, Mars is a giant desert today, with dust storms that sometimes cover the entire planet. Nevertheless there are many features on Mars that point to huge floods in its history, such as chasms, gullies, layered deposits, and shorelines, that flowing water can produce.[13] There is also evidence for glacial movement and even geysers.[14] Secular scientists even refer to a 'Noachian epoch' on Mars, named after the southern land mass Noachis Terra, in turn meaning 'land of Noah'.

At the very least, many scientists agree that Mars was once much wetter. In 2001, NASA announced, "Mars may once have been a very wet place. A host of clues remain from an earlier era, billions of years ago, hinting that the Red Planet was host to great rivers, lakes and perhaps even an ocean."[15] More recently, geographers

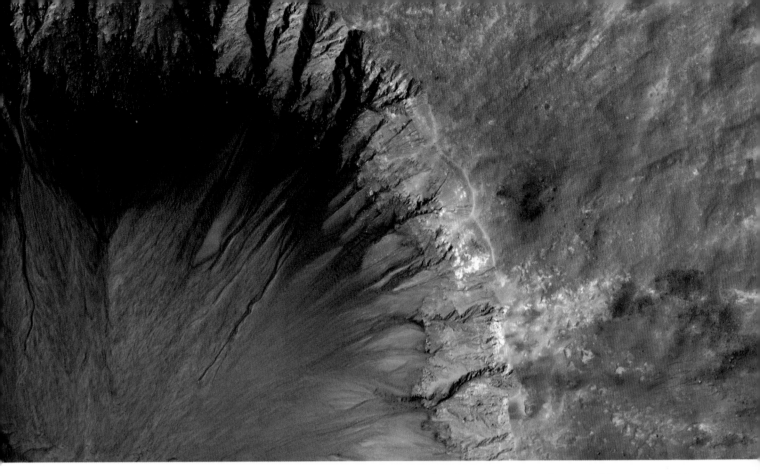

The High Resolution Imaging Science Experiment (HiRISE) camera aboard NASA's *Mars Reconnaissance Orbiter* acquired this close-up image of a 1-km-wide impact crater in the Sirenum Fossae (south-west) region of Mars. The sharp rim and well-preserved ejecta indicate a recent age.

have analyzed an advanced map generated by computer from satellite images. They concluded that there was a giant ocean in the northern hemisphere, fed by an extensive river network, in turn fed by rainfall.[16,17]

Yet water on Mars would have had a very low boiling point because of the very low atmospheric pressure (about 1% of Earth's), and so could not have lasted long without evaporating, and there is no known limestone, which surely would have formed in a watery world with a $CO_2$-rich atmosphere.[18] All this points to a young age for Mars, not billions of years.

Despite this, evolutionists claim this water lasted for many, many millions of years. Why? Because they want to find life on other planets than Earth, and they need water and time to do it. However, liquid water, if found, would not prove the existence of life.

Louis Pasteur disproved the idea of spontaneous generation in 1862. And, indeed, water breaks down the large molecules needed for life. You need an Intelligent Designer to create life. Evolution cannot explain the origin of life on Earth without a Creator, yet evolutionists are continually looking for life somewhere else, as if that would help them solve this problem.

## Which planet had a global flood?

Mars doesn't have a *drop* of liquid water, but many secular geologists agree that there were huge floods on it. Conversely, Earth is 71% *covered* by water (and if all the mountains were flattened down and ocean bottoms raised so the solid surface was completely even, this water would cover the whole surface to 3 km deep), and yet those same geologists *deny* the possibility of a global flood on this planet. Why? Earth's Flood shows that God judges sin, and will do so again, but secularists don't want to admit their accountability to their Creator. Mars shows that they are willingly ignorant, as the Apostle Peter said (2 Peter 3:3–7).

# Mars Facts

| | |
|---|---|
| Mean distance from sun | $228 \times 10^6$ km (1.5 AU, i.e. cf. Earth) |
| Mass | $6.4217 \times 10^{23}$ kg (10.7% Earth) |
| Equatorial radius | 3396 km (~53% Earth) |
| Mean density | 3933 kg/m³ (71.3% Earth) |
| Surface gravity | 3.71 m/s² (37.9% Earth) |
| Equatorial escape velocity | 5.03 km/s (45% Earth) |
| Length of Mars day | 24 hours 39 minutes 35 seconds |
| Orbit around sun (year) | 687 Earth days = 1.88 Earth years |
| Surface temperature average | -63° C (-81.4° F) |
| Atmospheric composition | $CO_2$ 95.3%, $N_2$ 2.7%, Ar 1.6%, $O_2$ 0.13% (Earth $N_2$ 78%, $O_2$ 21%, Ar 0.9% ... $CO_2$ 0.04% ) |

Source: Mars Fact Sheet, NASA, updated 19 April 2016.

## Conclusion

Mars is an intriguing red heavenly object, created as a sign and a marker of times. And while many have hoped for life, it is an inhospitable, cold, dry world. Yet there is good evidence that it had huge flooding. Since Mars is not that much farther from the sun than Earth, and is freezing, it shows how finely God tuned the earth's orbit to support life.

## References and Notes

1. This chapter adapted and updated from Sarfati, J., *Creation* **32**(2):38–41, 2010; creation.com/mars-red-planet.
2. Spencer, W., The existence and origin of extrasolar planets, *J. Creation* **15**(1):17–25, 2001; creation.com/extrasolar.
3. Freeman, T., The Genesis 5 and 11 fluidity question, *J. Creation* **19**(2):83–90, 2005, creation.com/fluidity; Sarfati, J., Biblical chronogenealogies, *J. Creation* **17**(3):14–18, 2003, creation.com/chronogenealogy; Cosner, L., Can Christians believe 'dogmatically' that the earth is 6,000 years old? creation.com/dogmatic-6000-years, 19 December 2009.
4. Bergman, J., H.G. Wells: Darwin's disciple and eugenicist extraordinaire, *J. Creation* **18**(3):116–120, 2004; creation.com/wells.
5. For an overview, see Chapter 7, and for more detail, see Bates, G., *Alien Intrusion: UFOs and the Evolution Connection*, Creation Book Publishers, 2011.
6. Bates, G., The 'face' on Mars, *Creation* **31**(1):22–23, 2008; creation.com/aliens-in-your-bedroom.
7. See solarsystem.nasa.gov/missions/profile.cfm?Sort=Target&Target=Mars&Era=Present, accessed 5 November 2012.
8. David, L., Mars methane mystery: *Curiosity* rover may find new clues, *space.com*, 23 October 2012.
9. Madhusoodanan, J., Microbial stowaways to Mars identified, *Nature News*, 19 May 2014 | doi:10.1038/nature.2014.15249. See also Smith, S. *et al.*, *American Society for Microbiology*, 114th Annual Meeting, 17–20 May 2014, Boston, Massachusetts.
10. In fact it was my very first article for our magazine and journal: Life on Mars? Separating fact from fiction, *Creation* **19**(1):18–20, 1996, creation.com/marslife; Sarfati, J., Life from Mars? *J. Creation* **10**(3):293–296, 1996, creation.com/images/pdfs/tj/j10_3/j10_3_293-296.pdf.
11. A minimum genome consists of 387 protein-coding and 43 RNA-coding genes, and this would be very fragile; Glass, J., *et al.*, Essential genes of a minimal bacterium, *Proceedings of the National Academy of Science USA* **103**(2):425–430, 2006. See also Sarfati, J., *By Design*, Chapter 11, Creation Book Publishers, 2008.
12. Sarfati, J., Conclusive evidence for life from Mars? Remember last time! creation.com/mars, 15 May 2002.
13. Spencer, W., Mars' catastrophic geology, *J. Creation* **22**(2):10–11, 2008; creation.com/article/6950.
14. Shiga, D., Fizzy water powered 'super' geysers on ancient Mars, *New Scientist News*, 17 March 2008; space.newscientist.com.
15. The case of the missing Mars water, science.nasa.gov/headlines/y2001/ast05jan_1.htm, 30 June 2004.
16. Luo, W. and Stepinski. T., Computer-generated global map of valley networks on Mars, *Journal of Geophysical Research* **114**, 20 November 2009.
17. von Radowitz, J., Giant ocean covered Mars, new map reveals, *The Independent* (UK), 24 November 2009.
18. Bates, G., Water, water, where are you? Confusion reigns on the Martian surface, *Creation* **27**(3):23–26, 2005; creation.com/mars-water.

# Chapter 10

# Jupiter: king of the planets and testimony to our Creator

Jupiter, the fifth planet from the sun, is the largest planet in our solar system. It dwarfs the earth—over 1,300 Earths could fit inside Jupiter. Its mass is 2½ times that of all the other planets combined. It takes about 12 Earth years to orbit the sun, but (despite its size) rotates on its axis in about 10 hours—the shortest 'day' of any planet in the solar system. The existence of Jupiter poses enormous problems for evolutionists, as the evolutionary model contradicts multiple lines of evidence.

**Author: Spike Psarris**[1]

# The Jovian Planets

Jupiter · Saturn · Uranus · Neptune

**The four outer planets in the solar system are known as Jovian planets, meaning Jupiter-like. They are mostly composed of massive amounts of hydrogen and helium, and so they are also called gas giants. Uranus and Neptune are thought to also contain quantities of frozen water, ammonia, and methane, and so are also called ice giants.**

## A gas giant

Unlike Earth, which is mostly rock, Jupiter is mostly gas—about 90% hydrogen, about 10% helium, with traces of methane, ammonia, and water vapour, as well as of the inert gases argon, xenon and krypton. It is classified as a gas giant, along with the other so-called 'Jovian' (i.e. Jupiter-like) planets, Saturn, Uranus and Neptune). Jupiter is about five times as far from the sun as Earth is. Because of this vast distance, Jupiter appears in our night-time sky like a bright white star. However, thanks to its massive size, even a modest telescope will reveal that it isn't a star, but a planet—it looks like a disk, while stars look like points of light.

## Jupiter's Great Red Spot

Jupiter's most famous feature is its Great Red Spot. This is an enormous, violent high pressure storm system rotating counter-clockwise with a period of about seven days, located in the atmosphere of Jupiter's southern hemisphere. It is much wider than planet Earth, is the largest storm in the entire solar system, and has been raging continuously for hundreds of

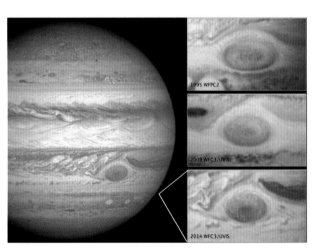

**Images of Jupiter's Great Red Spot taken by NASA's *Hubble Space Telescope* over the last 20 years show that the spot is shrinking in size, as well as changing shape.**

**A little red spot dubbed Red Spot Junior has appeared slightly below and to the left of the Great Red Spot. It formed from the merger of three smaller storms, and is similar in diameter to planet Earth.**

years. However, it appears to be now decreasing in size and changing shape.

In the late 19th century the spot was 48,000 km (30,000 miles) long. NASA *Voyager 1* and *Voyager 2* flybys of Jupiter in 1979 measured it to be 23,000 km (14,500 miles) across.[2] In 2009 it was 17,900 km (11,130 miles) across. NASA says: "Beginning in 2012, amateur observations revealed a noticeable increase in the rate at which the spot is shrinking—by 580 miles [930 km] per year—changing from an oval to a circle."[3]

In the past decade, several smaller oval-shaped storms merged to form another feature, officially named Oval BA. This has now changed colour from white to red and has been nicknamed Red Spot Junior.

## Jupiter's rings

Jupiter has a system of faint rings, first observed in 1979 by the *Voyager 1* space probe, and investigated by the Galileo orbiter in the 1990s, by the *Cassini* space probe in 2000, and again in 2007 by the *New Horizons* spacecraft. The largest available telescopes are needed to see the rings from Earth. They consist mainly of dust (unlike Saturn's rings which are mainly ice).

There is a thick inner ring of particles known as the 'halo ring'. Then a bright, very thin 'main ring' composed of particles believed to be fragments blasted by meteorites from the surface of moons Metis and Adrastea. Beyond this are two wide, thick and faint outer 'gossamer rings' named Amalthea and Thebe, after the moons of whose material they are thought to be composed.

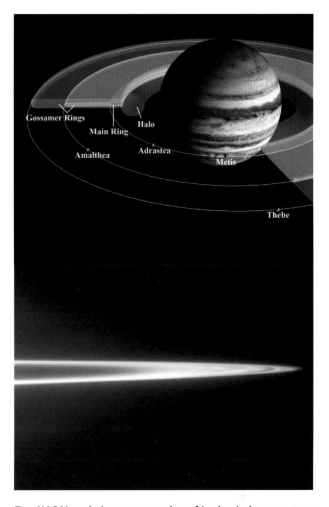

*Top:* NASA's artistic representation of Jupiter's ring structure and the moons affecting it (not to scale). *Bottom:* An image of the rings taken by *Voyager 2* from 1.5 million km. NASA's caption to this image says: "The rings are brightly lit by the forward scattered light from the sun, indicating that they are composed of very small particles. ... The main ring is about 125,000 km in diameter, and the inner glow is the halo ring."

## Jupiter's moons

Jupiter has four large moons, named (in order of closeness to Jupiter) Io, Europa, Ganymede and Callisto. They were the first natural satellites to be discovered, apart from our own moon. They are called the Galilean satellites, after Italian astronomer Galileo Galilei, who observed them in 1610 with his 30x magnification telescope.

They are spheroidal in shape and would be considered planets if they were in direct orbit around the sun. There are also another confirmed 63 smaller moons (at last count). Most of these are less than 10 km in diameter, of irregular shape, and have only been discovered since 1975.

**Io** is similar in size and composition to our moon, and is the most volcanically active body in the solar system. Its surface is covered by sulfur in different colourful forms, spewed from multiple volcanoes—over 400 have been counted,[4] of which at least 150 are currently active. Io generates the most heat for its size of any body in the solar system, except for the sun. Evolutionists were greatly surprised by this, as it should have become inert long ago—if it was billions of years old.

They attempt to explain it with theories of 'gravitational flexing' between Jupiter's huge mass on one side, and Jupiter's other large moons on the other. This accounts for some of the heat but not all, so where does the rest come from? If Io is young, it could

**Jupiter's four biggest moons, discovered by Galileo: from left to right, Io, Europa, Ganymede, and Calisto.**

still be cooling off from its creation. But if it is old, this energy should have dissipated long ago. So according to evolutionary theory, Io shouldn't have all the active volcanoes we see on its surface.

In fact, if Io were 4½ billion years old, it would have recycled itself, through its volcanoes, more than 30 times. Its mantle also would have differentiated, with higher-density materials sinking down to the core and lighter materials rising to the top—but this apparently has not occurred yet. Io does not look billions of years old, but it matches perfectly with the biblical account of creation 6,000 years ago.[5]

**Europa** appears to have a very smooth surface, in fact it is the smoothest natural body in the solar system. The entire surface is covered by a shell of ice several kilometres thick. It has very few impact craters, thus calling into question the billions of years it has supposedly been around for.

**Ganymede** is the largest moon in our solar system; it has a diameter of 5,262 km (3,270 miles), which is 151% of our own moon, and 8% larger than planet Mercury. Every time Ganymede orbits Jupiter once, Europa makes two orbits, and Io four. It is criss-crossed with grooves and ridges in weird patterns; some places are rough and rocky, others are flat and smooth. Evolutionary models predicted that it couldn't have a magnetic field, but space probes found that it did have one. Ganymede does not match the evolutionary model.

**Callisto** is almost an exact twin of Mercury in size and appearance. It is covered with craters or other signs of bombardment, more so than that of any other moon in

the solar system. Some pictures show what appears to be fresh ice on Callisto's surface, indicating that geological activity is still going on, i.e. it is not 'old, cold, and dead' as evolutionary models predict.

**Smaller moons**. NASA lists over 50 of these as having retrograde orbits,[6] i.e. they orbit Jupiter in a direction opposite to the rotation of Jupiter and hence to that of the other moons. This is another huge problem for the nebular hypothesis (see Chapter 1), and involves special pleading by evolutionists, such as that these moons were captured by Jupiter from solar orbits. However, for a space probe to go into orbit around a planet requires that it approach the planet at exactly the right angle, with very precise activation of the jets (by controllers at NASA or other headquarters) to de-accelerate the space vehicle, in order to prevent it either hitting the planet or being flung away from it.

In fact, scientists use this latter process, known as a gravitational slingshot or gravity assist, to increase the speed of a space probe (beyond the escape velocity with which it leaves Earth) once it is in orbit, and thereby speed it on its way in space. *Voyager 1* and *Voyager 2*, launched in 1977, both received gravity assist from Jupiter in 1979, to speed them on their way to Saturn and beyond. And *New Horizons* picked up 14,500 km/h (9,000 mph) in this way en route to Pluto on 28 February 2007.

The idea that some 50 moons of Jupiter could all have been travelling at precisely the right angle and correct velocity to go into orbit around Jupiter and thus avoid either hitting it or being slingshotted away into space defies rationality.

**An artist's concept of the space probe *Galileo* flying past a sulfur volcono on Jupiter's moon Io.**

## How can Jupiter exist?

The Romans named the planet after their chief deity, but where did this beautiful celestial orb come from? The Bible tells us that Jupiter, along with other heavenly objects, was created on Day 4 of Creation Week (Genesis 1:14–19). However, evolutionary astronomers deny the biblical account. They claim that Jupiter formed by natural processes about 4.5 billion years ago. Unfortunately for them, Jupiter poses enormous problems for those wishing to deny the creation of our solar system.

The standard evolutionary explanation for our solar system is that it formed from a swirling cloud of gas and dust. About 4.5 billion years ago, this cloud collapsed into a disk shape. The dust condensed into grains, the grains allegedly stuck together to become small rocks, and the small rocks stuck together to become larger rocks. But a major problem for this view is that fast moving rocks are more likely to bounce off each other rather than stick together.[7]

According to the evolutionists, the rocky planets like Venus and Earth formed as large rocks collected together. The gas giants like Jupiter and Saturn are said to have formed initially in the same way. But in contrast to the inner planets, the embryonic giant planets were far enough away from the sun for ice to condense. Therefore extra mass could accumulate in their core—involving over 10 times as much material as the entire Earth contains today. With the help of the ice, this accumulation had so much gravity that gas was pulled onto them, eventually forming the gas planets which we see today. Since this theory involves rocky chunks becoming the cores of the gas planets, this idea is called the 'core accretion' model.

This story is still being told today on television, in books and magazines, in science videos, and so on. However, scientists have known for a long time that this model doesn't fit the facts.

### A falsified model

The core accretion model has at least three fatal problems.

**Problem 1.** It makes definite predictions about the chemical composition of Jupiter. However, back in 1995, the *Galileo* spacecraft dropped a probe into Jupiter's atmosphere. Evolutionists were surprised to discover that Jupiter's atmosphere contained higher-than-expected amounts of the gases argon, xenon, and krypton. Evolutionary models say that these elements can't be there in such concentrations.[8]

As one report by an evolutionary astronomer explained: "Jupiter is the largest of all the planets. But results ... now reveal the embarrassing fact that we know next to nothing about how—or where—it formed."[9]

**Problem 2.** The model requires up to 10 million years for enough rocks and gas to accumulate to form Jupiter. But scientists also acknowledge that a disk of dust and gas wouldn't have lasted around our sun for that long. Many scientists believe that such a disk would have dissipated in less than 5 million years—leaving not enough time for Jupiter to form.[10]

**Problem 3.** Even if the gas/dust disk lasted long enough, we still wouldn't get a Jupiter from it. Recent computer simulations have revealed a fatal problem with the core accretion model. As gas giants formed within the disk, they would have interacted gravitationally with the dust remaining in the disk. It turns out that these interactions would pull the developing planets inward, towards the sun.

So both Jupiter and Saturn would have swirled inwards until they slammed into the sun. And this would have occurred 'quickly' in evolutionary terms: only 300,000 years after they started to form.

Obviously, according to evolution, Jupiter shouldn't be there at all.[11] It's no wonder that evolutionists make complaints like this one: "Building Jupiter has long been a problem for theorists."[12] Or this one: "I don't think the existence of Jupiter would be predicted if it weren't observed."[13]

Jupiter is a wonderful illustration of an important

principle in science: **When you reject the truth, you have to accept a fabrication.** Evolutionists have already rejected the biblical account of creation. Therefore, they have to accept the 'best' evolutionary alternative. Even though their model has been denied by multiple lines of evidence, it 'must' be true.

However, over and over again, the evolutionary model has been exposed to be false. As one evolutionist lamented, "... most every prediction by theorists about planetary formation has been wrong."[14] Another complained, "The thing we've learned in the last couple years is that the standard model cannot work."[15]

Yet evolutionists still cling to this model, despite the overwhelming evidence against it. They're unwilling to accept the truth that Jupiter illustrates about its Creator.

### Conclusion

Jupiter's huge size and position in the solar system are very positive evidences of design. With much more mass, and hence gravity, than all the other planets combined, Jupiter acts as a colossal cosmic vacuum cleaner, attracting stray comets, asteroids, and other space debris to crash into it rather than travelling on to the inner solar system, where Earth is located.

Truly, Jupiter's size, beauty, and grandeur are a wonderful testimony to our Creator—the God of the Bible, who not only made the stars and planets (for our benefit—Genesis 1:14-19), but also us!

**A map of Jupiter taken by *Cassini*; the South Pole is at the centre, the equator is at the edge.**

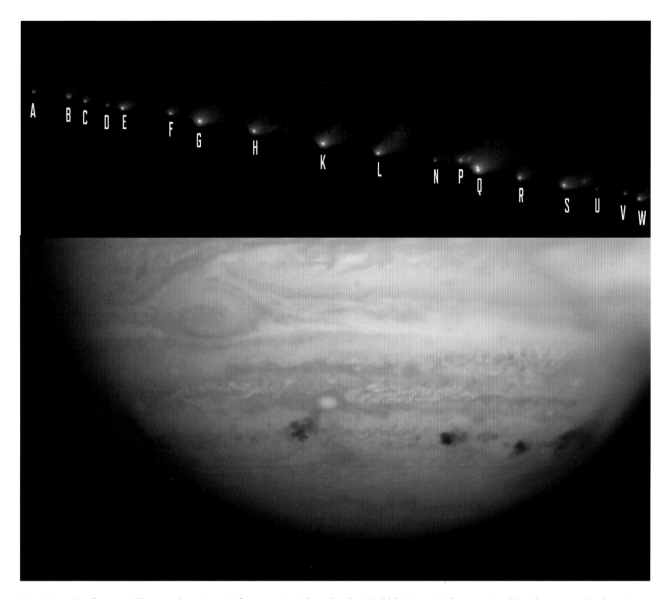

***Top:*** **Mosaic of comet Shoemaker–Levy 9 fragments taken by the *Hubble Space Telescope*. In this photograph, the pieces stretched across 1.1 million km of space. *Bottom:* The line of atmospheric scars on Jupiter was the result of successive hits by the comet fragments as Jupiter rotated.**

# The impact of comet Shoemaker–Levy 9 on Jupiter
## — the most spectacular event ever witnessed in the history of astronomy
### By Russell Grigg

According to *Encyclopædia Britannica*,[16] comet Shoemaker–Levy 9[17] was captured into orbit around Jupiter, probably back in 1929. Then on 8 July 1992, as it passed above Jupiter's atmosphere, Jupiter's immense gravity broke the comet's nucleus, estimated to be 1.6 km in diameter, into at least 20 discernible fragments and much smaller debris. The sun's gravity then changed the orbit of the fragments, causing them to impact the planet from 16 to 22 July 1994.

The fragments, strung out in a nearly straight line over 1.1 million km, smashed into Jupiter's atmosphere at intervals of seven to eight hours, with a velocity of 221,000 km/s (137,300 mph). The impacts were observed by the *Hubble Space Telescope*, and *Galileo*, *Ulysses*, and *Voyager 2* spacecraft,[18] and Jupiter's 9.92-hour rotation quickly brought each impact site into view to the many astronomers watching on Earth.

The fragments were labelled alphabetically in order

An artist's rendering of the NASA space probe *Juno*, which on 4 July 2016 entered a polar orbit around Jupiter after a 5-year trek from Earth. Scientists on Earth had to slow *Juno's* speed of 266,000 km/h (due to Jupiter's huge gravity) by exactly 542 metres per second, by means of a 35-minute engine burn, to allow this capture into orbit to take place.

# Jupiter Facts

| | |
|---|---|
| Mean distance from sun | $778.6 \times 10^6$ km (5.2 AU, i.e. cf. Earth) |
| Mass | $1,898.2 \times 10^{24}$ kg (317.83 × Earth) |
| Equatorial radius | 71,492 km (11.21 × Earth) |
| Polar radius | 66,854 km (10.517 × earth) |
| Mean density | 1,326 kg/m$^3$ (24% Earth) |
| Gravity | 24.79 m/s$^2$ (2.53 × Earth) |
| Equatorial escape velocity | 59.5 km/s (5.32 × Earth) |
| Length of Jupiter Day | 9.926 hours |
| Orbit around sun (i.e. year) | 11.86 Earth years |
| Mean temperature | -108° C |
| Atmosphere | $H_2$ 89.8%, He 10.2%, traces $CH_4$, $NH_3$, HD, $C_2H_6$ |
| Number of confirmed moons | 67 |

Source: Jupiter Fact Sheet, NASA, updated 19 April 2016.

of arrival. The largest, fragment G, estimated to be 350–600 metres in diameter, struck Jupiter with energy equivalent to at least 48 billion tons of TNT. The fragments did not produce craters on Jupiter because the planet does not have a solid surface. Rather, they plunged deep into the gas giant's atmosphere, creating massive 'bubbles' of super-hot gas that exploded in fireballs and plumes thousands of kilometres high, which deposited huge black clouds (some larger than Earth) on top of the Jovian clouds. These atmospheric 'scars' remained visible variously for weeks and months before eventually disappearing.

## References and Notes

1. This chapter adapted and updated from Psarris, S., *Creation* **30**(3):38–40, 2008; creation.com/jupiter.

2. Great Red Spot, *Encyclopaedia Britannica*, 2016.

3. NASA's Hubble Shows Jupiter's Great Red Spot is Smaller than Ever Measured, NASA News, May 15, 2014.

4. Williams, D.A. *et al.*, Volcanism on Io: New insights from global geologic mapping, *Icarus* **214**(1):91–112, July 2011.

5. *What You Aren't Being Told About Astronomy, Vol. 1, Our Created Solar System*, DVD.

6. NASA, Jovian Satellite Fact Sheet, updated 19 April 2016.

7. See also Sarfati, J., Earth is 'too special'? in Chapter 5.

8. According to the evolutionary model, these elements could only be present in such concentrations if Jupiter had formed further out in the solar system—at more than 10 times Jupiter's current distance from the sun. Some have suggested that maybe Jupiter formed at that distance, and then moved inwards later. However, this doesn't solve the problem. There wouldn't have been enough material at that distance for Jupiter to form. Also, Jupiter doesn't contain the heavy elements that it should have, if it had actually formed way out there.

9. Ball. P., Giant mistake, *Nature science update*, 18 November 1999; nature.com/news/1999/991118/full/news991118-10.html.

10. There have been multiple attempts to solve this problem. One approach is to arbitrarily assume different properties for certain initial conditions, e.g. that dust opacity around Jupiter was 50 times less than current interstellar dust opacities. This lower opacity supposedly resulted in more rapid heat loss from and more rapid contraction of the proto-planetary envelope. This shortens the time required to make Jupiter in the models, but it doesn't match actual observations we make today. Another approach is to propose a completely different way to build Jupiter; the most prominent of these is the 'disk instability' model, which claims that Jupiter formed quickly from a large clump in the dust disk. This idea has many problems and is controversial even among secular researchers..

11. Recent attempts to solve the migration problem have only made matters worse. One suggested answer is that Jupiter is only the last of a series of gas giant planets, each of which did migrate inwards into the sun. Jupiter was merely the last one in the series, which happened to form right as the gas/dust disk was dissipating. Even many evolutionists are bothered by the obviously *ad hoc* nature of this fable—there's no evidence for it, and its only purpose is to rescue evolution from the facts. Plus, Jupiter couldn't have formed from a disk that was depleted by previous generations of gas giant formation. So this suggested solution solves nothing. The 'disk instability' model is invoked again here. Its proponents claim that the gas/dust disk collapsed quickly into planets, before migration could occur. This model has a long list of fatal problems: Uranus and Neptune don't match its predictions, the comets and other trans-Neptunian objects don't match its predictions, and the model's proponents have yet to demonstrate that rapid disk collapse is even possible anyway.

12. Wetherill, G.W., How special is Jupiter? *Nature* **373**(6514):470, 9 February 1995.

13. Wetherill, G.W., *The Formation and Evolution of Planetary Systems*, Cambridge University, p. 27, 1989, as quoted in Stuart Ross Taylor, *Solar System Evolution: A New Perspective*, Cambridge University Press, Cambridge, UK, p. 205, 2001.

14. Scott Tremaine, as quoted by Kerr, R.A., Jupiters like our own await planet hunters, *Science* **295**(5555):605, 25 January 2002.

15. Harold Levison of the Southwest Research Institute as quoted in *Solar system makeover: wild new theory for building planets*, space.com/scienceastronomy/solarsystem/planet_formation_020709-2.html, 9 November 2007.

16. Weissman, P., Comet Shoemaker–Levy 9, *Encyclopædia Britannica*, downloaded 5 March, 2016.

17. So named because it was the ninth short-period comet discovered by Eugene and Carolyn Shoemaker and David Levy. This they did on March 25, 1993.

18. Williams D, Comet Shoemaker–Levy 9 Collision with Jupiter, NASA, 4 February 2005.

**An image of smooth ice-covered Europa, to which an artist has added a concept of NASA's Europa mission spacecraft planned for the mid 2020s.**

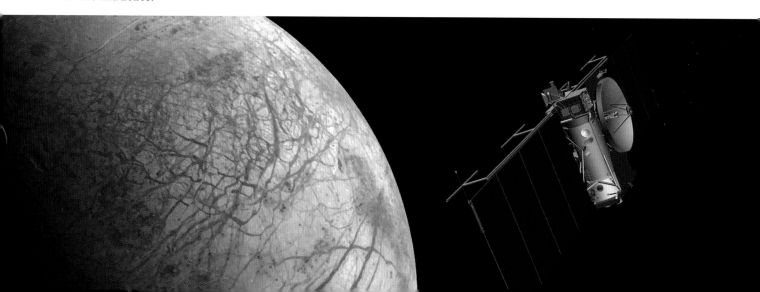

# Chapter 11

# Saturn: the ringed planet

Saturn is the sixth planet out from our sun, and is bigger than any other planet except Jupiter. It is classified as a gas giant, being over 760 times the volume of Earth. It is probably best known for its rings, which are among the most beautiful objects in the entire solar system. Its main components are ~96% hydrogen, ~3% helium, and ~0.4% methane. Wind speeds in its upper atmosphere can reach 1,440 km/h (1,100 mph). It takes 29.42 Earth years to orbit the sun, but its rotation or 'day' is only 10 hours 39 minutes 21.6 seconds.

Author: Spike Psarris[1]

Because of the dense pressure at the core, some of the hydrogen is thought to be metallic (a form of liquid hydrogen that is a good electric conductor). This is surrounded by liquid and gaseous hydrogen and helium.

The upper atmosphere is thought to contain ammonia ice crystals which contribute the pale yellow colour to the planet, as well as traces of sulfur, methane, and nitrogen that provide the colourful bands. Like Jupiter and Neptune, Saturn radiates much more energy into space than it receives from the sun.

## The origin of Saturn

Where did this wonderful planet, named after the Roman god of agriculture, Saturn, come from? The Bible tells us that everything we see in the sky, which would include Saturn, was made on Day 4 of Creation Week (Genesis 1:14–19). This was about 6,000 years ago.

Evolutionary astronomers tell us that Saturn, along with the other planets in our solar system, formed from a cloud of gas and dust about 4.5 billion years ago. Which is true?

The standard evolutionary astronomy model contradicts the Bible in almost every way possible. Therefore, we know that the evolutionary model can't be true. As the Word of God, the Bible stands on its own authority, contradictory accounts are wrong by definition. And the evidence confirms this truth. Like every other planet in our solar system, Saturn is a wonderful testimony to its recent creation.

## The rings of Saturn

Saturn's rings are among the most famous sights in all of astronomy. A few other planets have rings, but none are as prominent—or as beautiful—as Saturn's. In a small telescope, Saturn appears to have one solid ring. However, we now know that Saturn has many thousands of rings, nested one inside another, in seven major ring divisions, which orbit at different speeds around the planet. These have been given letter names A to G in the order of their discovery.

Working outward from the planet, the rings are D, C, B, A, F, G and E. Rings A, B, and C are the most visible; the others are thin and faint. The (innermost) D ring begins 66,900 km from Saturn's centre and is 7,610 km wide; the E ring begins 180,000 km from the centre and is 300,000 km wide. Each major ring division is made up of thousands of individual ringlets. In the B-ring there are also recurring patterns of 'spokes', thought to consist of tiny charged particles that have become trapped within the lines of Saturn's magnetic field. The F ring appears braided. Much of this structure is still a mystery.

**An eclipse of the sun by Saturn taken by the *Cassini* spacecraft in orbit around Saturn. It shows the rings in a new light, including the faint E ring, the ring formed by the ice-fountains of the moon Enceladus.**

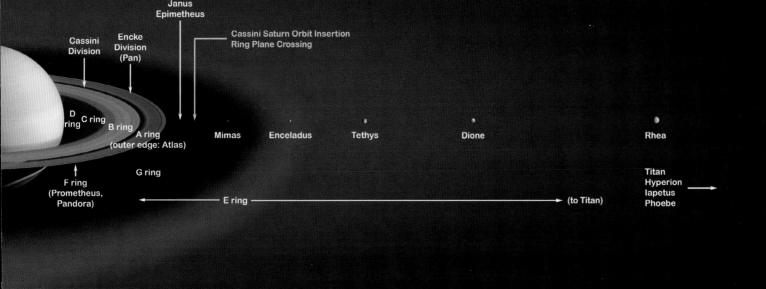

**Saturn's A-G rings. The moon Enceladus produces the materials that compose the E ring.**

**This artistic representation of the recently discovered giant 'Phoebe ring' around Saturn simulates an infrared view. This is the frequency at which the ring emits thermal energy, which our eyes cannot see unaided. It contains the moon Phoebe.**

The rings are made up of billions of particles, all orbiting the planet together. The smallest particles are grains of dust, while the largest are house-sized boulders. They are primarily composed of ice. It was the great creationist physicist James Clerk Maxwell who first showed in 1850 that the rings had to be composed of particles, not a solid sheet or liquid.[2] Compared to their width, Saturn's rings are razor-thin (only 20 m (65 ft) average thickness). If we were to build a scale model of the rings, making the model the size of a large city, the rings would be only as thick as a sheet of paper.

In 2009, NASA announced that the infrared *Spitzer Space Telescope*, currently in orbit around the sun, had discovered the huge, never-before-seen 'Phoebe ring' around Saturn.[3] The ring begins about 6 million km from Saturn and extends outward for about another 12 million km. It is extremely tenuous, with only about 20 grains of ice and dust particles per cubic kilometre, and so reflects very little light, which is why it hasn't been seen until now. It was detected by the infrared radiation it emits. Saturn's moon, Phoebe, orbits within this ring and is thought to be the source of the material. The new ring's orbit is tilted 27 degrees from Saturn's main ring plane, like Phoebe's, and its orbital motion is retrograde, also like Phoebe's.

## Saturn's moons

Saturn has 62 moons with confirmed orbits, as well as hundreds of known moonlets embedded in its rings, and countless smaller icy objects that form Saturn's ring system. Most of Saturn's moons are very small, e.g. 49 are less than 50 km in diameter.

Moons that orbit inside rings and appear to be responsible for defining the boundaries of their rings are called shepherd rings. The narrow F-ring has the small satellites Prometheus and Pandora orbiting just inside it and outside it. Prometheus is thought to contribute to the narrowness of the ring, and may also be responsible for the twists and kinks in its strands.

Some of Saturn's moons have retrograde orbits, i.e. they orbit Saturn opposite to Saturn's rotation. The largest of these, Phoebe, is about 200 km in diameter. Retrograde moons are a huge problem for evolutionary theory. Other moons with features best explained as being young rather than billions of years old are Titan and Enceladus. See below.

## Titan: the moon that contradicts evolution theory[4]

Saturn's largest moon is called Titan. It is the second largest moon in the solar system (Jupiter's Ganymede is the largest). Titan is 148% the diameter of Earth's

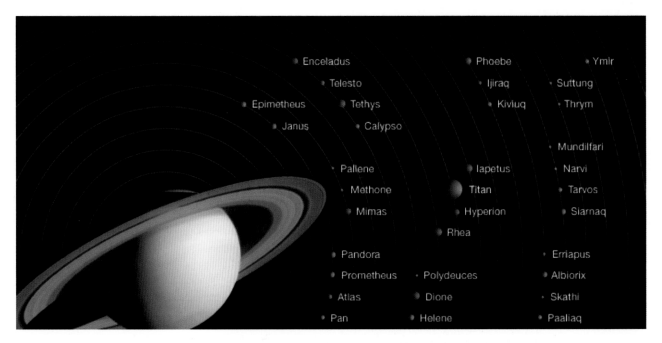

**NASA's artistic representation of about half of Saturn's main moons in their relative orbits.**

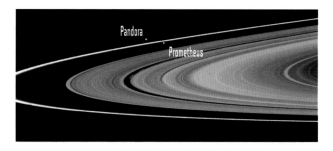

**Two satellites sandwiching the F ring in this *Cassini* image are the shepherd moons Prometheus (inner) and Pandora (outer). They orbit about 1,000 km on either side of the ring.**

**Titan. The dark areas are thought to be lakes of liquid methane and ethane, but are far short of the amount predicted by evolutionary theory. Notice the smooth surface of the rest of this moon and the lack of impact craters.**

Credit: NOAA/NASA/ESA

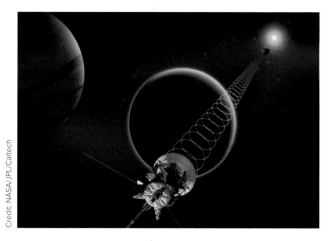

**An artist's concept of the *Cassini* spacecraft flying past Saturn's moon Titan, and sending signals back to Earth.**

Credit: NASA/JPL/Caltech

moon and makes up 96 percent of the mass in orbit around Saturn. It has an atmosphere of mostly nitrogen with some methane. This methane poses huge problems for evolutionary theory. This is because sunlight decomposes methane, forming ethane and other chemicals. There is still lots of methane there today, so if Titan were billions of years old, there should be lots of ethane there also.

Evolutionists confidently predicted that the *Cassini* spacecraft would reveal a global ocean of liquid methane and ethane on Titan. One report suggested it would be 800 metres deep; another predicted an average depth of several kilometres. The *Cassini* pictures showed Titan's surface to be dry, with some isolated dark areas that could be lakes of methane or ethane, but grossly inadequate to fulfil evolution's billions-of-years requirements.

Another problem for evolutionary theory is that because Titan's surface is solid, it should have thousands of impact craters—if it were 4.5 billion years old. By the time *Cassini* had mapped 10% of Titan's surface, it had found only four.

Titan doesn't look billions of years old, it looks young. It is a great demonstration of the failure of evolution theory.

## Enceladus: Saturn's sprightly moon looks young.[5]

NASA's spacecraft flybys of Saturn's tiny moon Enceladus have revealed an active world that continues to confound evolutionist scientists.[6] The images returned to Earth show the moon is about 504 km (313 miles) in diameter; it is covered in water ice that reflects almost 100% of the light it receives from the sun, and so the surface is not only bright but also extremely cold, about -200° C (-330° F).

The *Cassini* spacecraft cameras were turned toward Enceladus in 2005, with surprising results. Most scientists expected all Saturn's moons to be cold and dead, and their surfaces to be covered with impact craters from exposure to meteors for billions of years. Instead, Enceladus is mostly smooth. Scientists still asserted that the moon was billions of years old, but said it must have acquired a *new* surface in the recent past. NASA scheduled more *Cassini* flybys to investigate.[7]

Credit: NASA/JPL/Caltech/Space Science Institute

**Top:** Enceladus (arrowed) is miniscule in size compared with its planet Saturn. This tiny moon is far too small to have retained its heat for billions of years. *Middle:* Artist's concept of the 'tiger stripes' (colourized) that straddle the south pole of Enceladus, with *Cassini* spacecraft flying by. *Below:* The geologically active 'tiger stripes' spray plumes of water vapour and ice crystals (colourized) hundreds of kilometres into space. This material forms the E-ring.

The spacecraft also captured close-up images of four distinctive, 'tiger-stripe' fractures that straddle the south polar region of Enceladus. They are 130 km (80 miles) long × 500 m (1,600 ft) deep, about 40 km (25 miles) apart, and have been named Alexandria, Cairo, Baghdad, and Damascus (after cities referred to in *The Arabian Nights*)[8] These fractures act like vents and blast powerful curtain-like geysers of water vapour and tiny ice particles hundreds of kilometres into space, at the rate of 100 kg per second.[9] Infrared measurements have estimated the energy produced by the geysers to be 5.8 gigawatts—enough to power a city with 6 million people. Contrary to all expectation, NASA's news release of 30 August 2005 says the stripes are "between 10 and 1,000 years young".[10] According to evolutionary theory, Enceladus should have long since been dead, but obviously it is still geologically active.

This tiny moon seems to have an enormous influence on the whole ring system of Saturn. The jets produce the material for the outer E ring. The gas from the jets is also ionized and tends to drag the magnetosphere so strongly that it distorts our measurements of Saturn's rotation. And even more surprisingly, the plasma cloud around Saturn is being drawn into the brighter A ring, much closer to the planet.

## How can such a small moon have enough heat to power the geysers?

One suggestion was that radioactive substances inside the moon are heating it. But even though Enceladus is the rockiest of Saturn's major moons, it could not contain enough radioactive material to produce the observed heat.[11]

Another idea is that the gravitational pull of Saturn changes the shape of Enceladus as it orbits every 1.37 days. It heats the moon like a metal wire heats when you bend it backwards and forwards. But if so, why is Enceladus still flexible? When James Roberts and Francis Nimmo of the University of California modelled the moon's interior, they found it would have frozen after only 30 million years—less than 1% of its supposed age.[12]

What about the effects of Enceladus' out-of-round orbit imposed on it by Dione (a larger nearby moon of Saturn)? Again, no. Still not enough heat.[13]

Perhaps Enceladus obtained the heat when Saturn

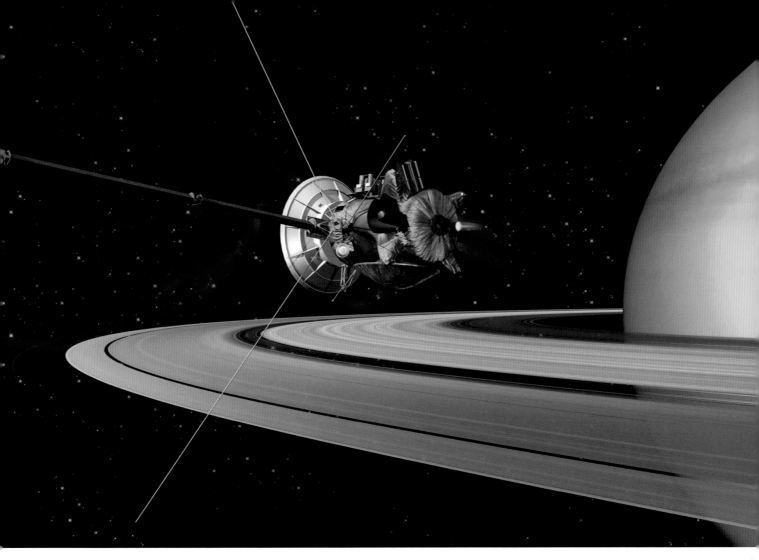

**The unexpectedly sharp edges of Saturn's ringlets, as revealed by *Cassini*, are evidence that our solar system is only thousands of years old, not billions—there hasn't been enough time for the edges to become smooth.**

and its moons formed, and it has not cooled down yet. This is a logical conclusion, but that would mean Saturn and its moons are not billions of years old. In fact, this enigmatic moon of Saturn fits beautifully with a solar system created just 6,000 years ago as biblical history records.

### According to evolution, Saturn can't be here at all.

Saturn defies evolution in many ways. For example, scientists have discovered that Saturn's magnetic field is symmetrical around its spin axis. According to the billions-of-years theories, this cannot be.[14] Therefore, Saturn cannot be billions of years old.

But that isn't the worst problem Saturn poses for those who wish to deny the biblical account of creation. Along with Jupiter, Saturn is a 'gas giant' planet. The ringed planet is mostly hydrogen gas, and has a very low density of 0.687 gm/cm³. It is the only planet in the solar system with a density of less than 1

gm/cm³. Saturn would float on water—if you could find a big enough bathtub![15]

But the evolutionary model says gas giants shouldn't exist at all. The evolutionary explanation for our solar system is that all the planets formed from a swirling cloud of gas and dust. These supposedly condensed into tiny particles, which stuck together to become rocks, which stuck together to become planets.

However, this idea has several fatal flaws.[16] First of all, nobody can figure out how the particles would stick together to become rocks. They would be too small for their gravity to overcome the force of the collisions.

More to the point, gas-giant protoplanets wouldn't last in this environment. Studies show that the cores of both Saturn and Jupiter would have moved inwards as the planets were forming, smashing into the sun. See also A falsified model: Problem 3, re Jupiter, Chapter 10.

Astronomers call this the 'migration problem'—if the

**An artist's concept of the *Cassini* orbiter crossing Saturn's ring plane.**

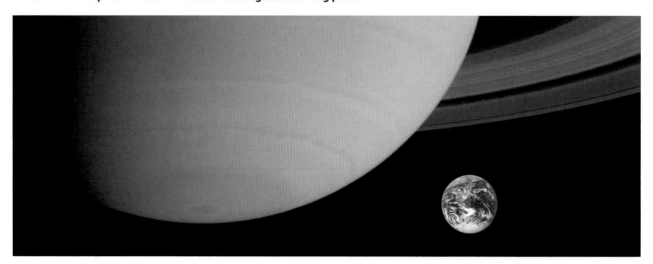

**Saturn and Earth shown to scale.**

gas and dust model were true, both planets would have migrated into our sun billions of years ago. Neither Jupiter nor Saturn would exist today. However, we see both planets in our solar system. This obviously creates a problem for evolution. As one report explained: "Theories predict that the giant protoplanets will merge into the central star before planets have time to form. This makes it very difficult to understand how they can form at all."[17]

That's why evolutionists are making complaints like this one: "For scientists who spend time thinking about how planets form, life would be simpler if gas giants like Jupiter and Saturn didn't exist."[18]

Or this one: "Talk about a major embarrassment for planetary scientists. There, blazing away in the late evening sky, are Jupiter and Saturn—the gas giants that account for 93% of the solar system's planetary mass—and no one has a satisfying explanation of how they were made."[19]

The evolutionary model fails utterly to explain Saturn. Conversely, the Creation model fits Saturn perfectly. As the Bible explains, this spectacular planet was made (along with the other heavenly objects) for signs and seasons (Genesis 1:14). It was also made to "declare the glory of God" (Psalm 19:1)—and this it does very well indeed!

Saturn tells us that our Creator is not only majestic and powerful—He appreciates beauty as well.

# Saturn Facts

| | |
|---|---|
| Mean distance from the sun | 1,433.5 million km (9.58 AU, i.e. cf. Earth) |
| Mass | $568.34 \times 10^{24}$ kg (95.16 × Earth) |
| Equatorial radius | 60,268 km (9.45 × Earth) |
| Mean density | 0.687 g/cm$^3$ (12.5% Earth) |
| Equatorial escape velocity | 35.5 km/s (3.17 × Earth) |
| Length of Saturn day | 10.66 hours (44.4% Earth) |
| Orbit around sun (i.e. year) | 29.42 Earth years |
| Mean temperature | -139° C, (-220° F) |
| Atmosphere | $H_2$ 96.3%, He 3.25%, + traces of $CH_4$, $NH_3$, HD, $C_2H_6$ |

Source: Jupiter Fact Sheet, NASA, updated 19 April 2016.

## References and Notes

1.  This chapter adapted and updated from Psarris, S., *Creation* **30**(4):18–20, 2009; creation.com/saturn.
2.  Lamont, A., James Clerk Maxwell (1831–1879), *Creation* **15**(3):45–47, 1993; creation.com/maxwell.
3.  Grayson, M., Huge 'ghost' ring discovered around Saturn, nature.com/news, 7 October 2009.
4.  This section adapted from Psarris, S., What you aren't being told about Astronomy, Vol. 1, Our Solar System, DVD
5.  This section authored by Tas Walker, *Creation* **31**(3):54–55, 2009; creation.com/enceladus-looks-young.
6.  Vittorio, S., *Cassini* visits Enceladus—new light on a bright world, csa.com, July 2006.
7.  Porco, C., The restless world of Enceladus, *Scientific American* **299**(6):26–35, p. 26, December 2008.
8.  New names for Enceladus, Astrogeology Science Center, 13 Nov. 2006.
9.  Enceladus plume is a new kind of plasma laboratory, NASA, 1 June 2012.
10. Cassini finds Enceladus tiger stripes are really cubs, NASA Mission News, 08.30.05, 2005-139.
11. Ref. 7, p. 31.
12. Schirber, M., Frigid future for ocean in Saturn's moon, *Astrobiology Magazine*, 19 June 2008; space.com.
13. Ref. 7, p. 32.
14. Evolutionists believe that planetary magnetism is caused by 'dynamos' deep inside each planet. This is the only way that a planet could still have a magnetic field after billions of years. One of the requirements for a dynamo is that the magnetic field can't line up with the spin axis. However, Saturn's does. "Saturn first dumbfounded planetary theorists who study dynamo models by having a highly symmetric internal magnetic field. A field that is symmetric about the rotation axis violates a basic theorem of magnetic dynamos." Bagenal, F., A new spin on Saturn's rotation, *Science* **316** (5823):380–381, 20 April 2007. Thus, Saturn's magnetic field can't be coming from a dynamo—which means it isn't billions of years old. Saturn's magnetic field looks quite young.
15. This is a useful metaphor for highlighting Saturn's low density, but the bathtub of water would actually compress and merge with Saturn.
16. See also Sarfati, J., Earth is 'too special'? in Chapter 5.
17. *Astronomy & Astrophysics press release*, The locked migration of giant protoplanets, aanda.org/index.php?option=com_content&id=92, 21 March 2006.
18. Than, K., Death spiral: why theorists can't make solar systems, space.com, 9 November 2007.
19. Kerr. R.A., A quickie birth for Jupiters and Saturns, *Science* **298**(5599):1698–1699, 29 November 2002.

# Chapter 12

# Uranus: the strange planet

## It provides an exciting testimony to the Creator

Uranus is the seventh planet from our sun and the third largest (by volume) in the solar system. Perhaps more than any other planet, Uranus and its moons pose big problems for theories of planet formation that try to dismiss a Creator. It is tipped on its side, and its moons orbit almost perpendicular to the plane of the ecliptic. However, it shows no sign of the alleged collision that supposedly caused this to happen.

**Author: Spike Psarris**[1]

The atmosphere of Uranus is made up of about 82.5% hydrogen, 15.2% helium, and 2.3% methane. It is bluish green because frozen methane crystals in its atmosphere absorb red light.[2] It is about 64 times the size of Earth by volume. At 19 times the distance from the sun to Earth, Uranus is so far away that it takes almost 84 Earth-years to orbit the sun once, but one rotation takes only 17.24 hours. Storm winds can blow at up to 900 km/h.

It was discovered in 1781, when famed British astronomer William Herschel, a Christian, noted an uncharted bright object traversing an area of sky he was studying with his 6-inch telescope. German astronomer Johann Bode named it Uranus after the god of the heavens from Greek mythology, Ouranos (Οὐρανός). All the other planets apart from Earth are named after Roman gods.

## Problems for evolution

Much of our information about Uranus and its moons was obtained from the *Voyager 2* spacecraft, when it flew by the planet in January 1986. Even before *Voyager 2*, scientists knew that some of Uranus's

characteristics caused problems for naturalistic theories. By 1948, it was known that Uranus had at least five moons, but their orbits were not at all what had been expected. The moons' orbits were discovered to be perpendicular to the 'ecliptic' (the plane in which most of the planets orbit the sun). This meant that either the moons were orbiting Uranus around its poles instead of its equator, or else the rotational axis of Uranus itself was inclined a long way over compared to the other planets. The latter turned out to be the case.

Uranus's equator is almost perpendicular to the ecliptic.[3] For this reason, for part of its orbit, the 'north' pole of Uranus faces the sun, and then for a different part of its orbit the 'south' pole faces the sun (see diagram.) The polar periods of light and darkness are 42 years long.

This situation is impossible according to evolutionary ideas about the formation of the solar system, namely that the planets condensed from a rotating nebula (see Chapter 1). Uranus cannot have formed this way naturally. What then is the evolutionists' solution? Most of them believe that Uranus did actually form the 'correct' way, i.e. according to

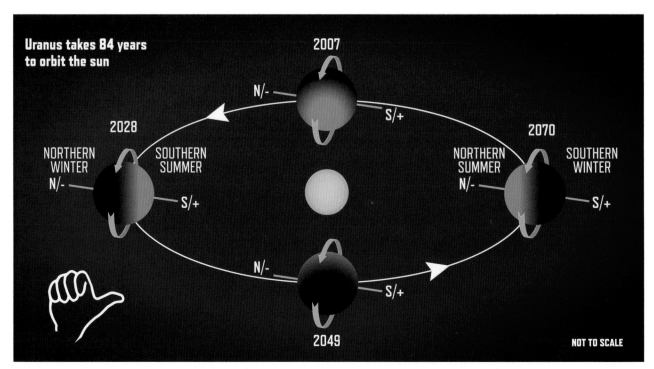

**Uranus is tipped on its side at an angle of ~98°. The International Astronomical Union defines the north pole of a planet as the pole which is above the ecliptic (the plane of the earth's orbit). But according to the right-hand rule, when the fingers of the right hand are curled around in the direction of a planet's rotation, the thumb points in the direction of the positive pole. Both designations are shown in the diagram.**

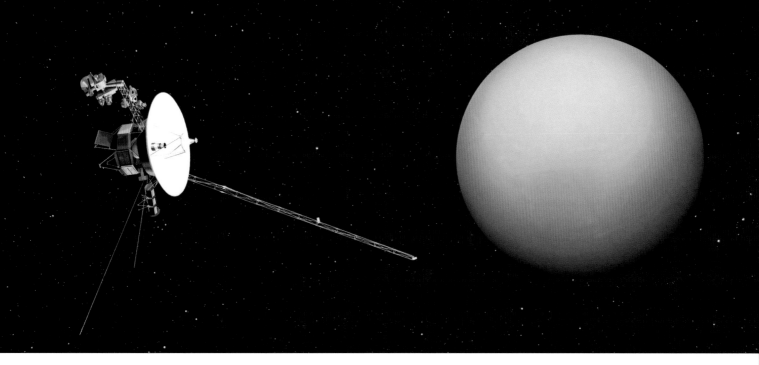

**An artist's concept of *Voyager 2* encountering Uranus.**

evolution, but then was subsequently knocked over during a collision with another planet, supposedly the size of Earth. It is claimed, "Models for the development of the solar system cannot produce such an orientation without invoking a collision with another object."[4]

## How feasible is this explanation?

First of all, Uranus's orbit shows no sign of such a catastrophic collision. Its orbit is one of the most circular of all the planets (only Venus, Earth and Neptune have orbits that are more circular). A collision would have much more likely resulted in a more elliptical orbit. Also, the plane of Uranus's orbit lies more closely within the ecliptic plane (the plane of Earth's orbit around the sun) than that of any other planet. A massive collision should have disturbed the planet's orbit more than this.

Furthermore, the moons of Uranus pose many problems all by themselves. Today, they are orbiting around the planet's equator, which is approximately at a right angle to the ecliptic. Obviously, these moons could not have been present when the supposed Earth-size object hit Uranus, because the moons would have been scattered or disrupted, and would not have quietly moved into stable orbits that are now inclined 98 degrees away from their alleged previous orbits. Therefore, reasons the evolutionist, the moons must have formed after the impact, and the moons that we see today are actually the fragments left over from the impact.

However, all of the moons combined, plus the particles in the small rings around Uranus, constitute only about 0.01% of the mass of the planet. This puts a severe limitation on the size of any collision that produced such a small amount of debris. An impact violent enough to push Uranus over presumably would have produced much more debris than this—indeed, a currently fashionable idea about the formation of Earth's moon uses a collision of a comparable relative scale to 'produce' a moon with 1.2% of Earth's mass.[5]

Finally, this idea of a catastrophic impact implies more than a little hypocrisy among the evolutionists. They mock Christians for accepting the biblical account of a global Flood (an event for which there is abundant physical evidence), because it was a one-time catastrophe. We are told that such catastrophes are unrepeatable, and are therefore 'unscientific'. Yet here we see that evolutionists invoke one-off planetary catastrophes with impunity, to overcome multiple problems within their own belief system.

## A problem about energy

As one of the four Jovian 'gas giant' planets (Jupiter, Saturn, Uranus and Neptune), Uranus poses yet another problem for naturalism. The other three gas giants all generate energy (i.e. they radiate considerably more heat into space than they receive from the sun). Uranus is alone in failing to do this. How can this be? If naturalistic processes formed the solar system without a Creator, then the products of these processes should be very similar. In particular, Uranus and Neptune are very similar in size, atmospheric composition, rotation rate, and location in the solar system. One would then expect that they would be similar in other major characteristics as well—but Neptune radiates into space more than twice the energy it receives, while it is disputed whether or not Uranus radiates any excess energy at all.[6]

## Magnetic field

If all of this wasn't bad enough, evolutionists received a further series of rude shocks when *Voyager 2* flew by the Uranus system in 1986, taking many photographs and measurements. "To the complete astonishment of scientists, the magnetic axis [of Uranus] is tilted approximately 60 degrees with respect to its axis of rotation. It is not known why."[7]

The strength of the magnetic field was also a surprise to evolutionists, though not to creationists, as creationist astrophysicist Dr Russell Humphreys, using biblical assumptions, had accurately predicted the strength two years previously![8]

In order to sustain belief in millions of years, evolutionists need to try to overcome the problem that Earth's magnetic field, like all physical systems, is gradually decaying. Calculations indicate that it would not be here anymore if the Earth were more than a few thousand years old.[9] So they assume a complicated 'dynamo' model of planetary magnetic fields, to try to have the field sustain itself from the planet's motion. However, when this is applied to Uranus, both the strength of Uranus's field and the fact that its magnetic and rotational axes are so far apart defy the predictions of this evolutionary dynamo model.

## Uranus's rings

Uranus is known to have 13 distinct rings, the second such system to be discovered in the solar system after that of Saturn. The majority are only a few kilometres wide and are composed of particles a few centimetres to 10 metres in diameter. Their composition is not known for sure. The rings are narrow, separated by wide gaps and so are distinctly different from the faint dusty rings of Jupiter or the broad, complex, highly visible ones of Saturn.

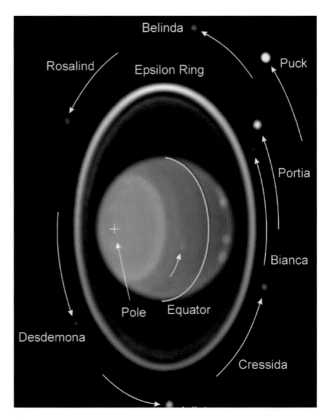

**Uranus is tipped 98° on its side, so the rings and moons that orbit its equator are at this same angle to the ecliptic.**

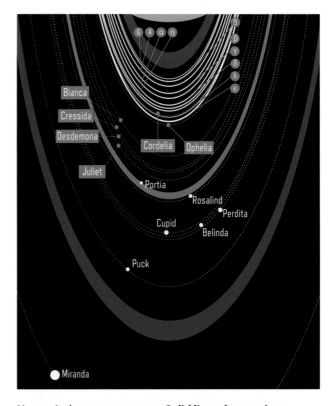

**Uranus's ring-moon system. Solid lines denote rings; dashed lines denote orbits of moons.**

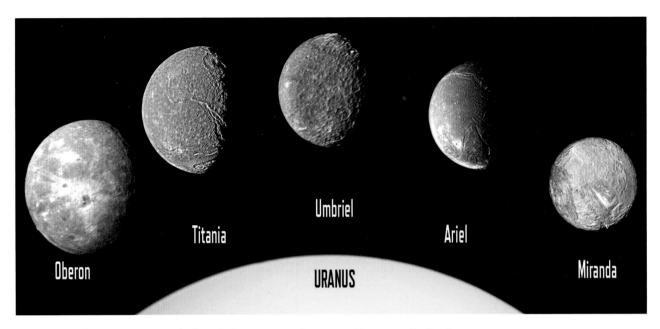

The moons of Uranus are named after Shakespearean characters. These are the five largest.

## Uranus's moons

*Voyager 2* discovered more moons around Uranus than were previously known. We now know of 27, all of them named after characters in the works of William Shakespeare and Alexander Pope. Many are icy with no atmosphere or magnetosphere. Two of the innermost moons, Ophelia and Cordelia, shepherd the Episolon ring.

## Miranda

As a consequence of NASA using *Voyager 2*'s flypast of Uranus as a gravitational boost to propel the spacecraft onwards to Neptune, *Voyager 2* happened to fly very close to the smallest moon, Miranda. Since Miranda is so tiny (having a diameter of about 470 km, only 13.5% of the diameter of Earth's moon), scientists expected it to be a small, boring chunk of ice. Instead, it has

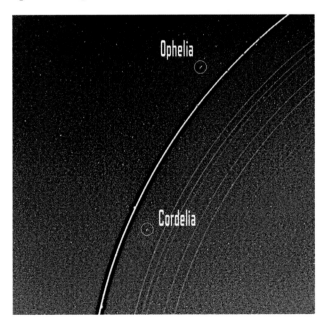

***Voyager 2*** found that two of the innermost moons of Uranus, Cordelia and Ophelia, orbit on either side of the Epsilon ring at exactly the right radii required for shepherding.

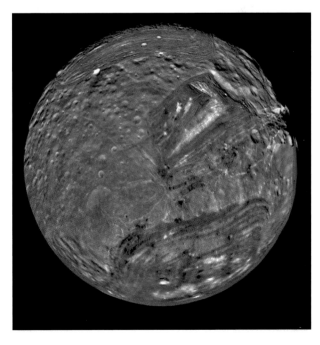

**Miranda has a spectacular array of dissimilar features that confound evolutionists' explanations.**

**A section of Miranda about 250 km across. On the right is rugged high-elevation terrain and to the left a lower, striated area.**

proven to be one of the strangest objects in our solar system.

It has huge fault canyons up to 20 km (12 miles) deep, terraced layers, fractures, grooves, craters, and both old-looking and young-looking surface features. With one sheer cliff reaching nearly 10 km (6 miles) high, Miranda has some of the most dramatic terrain in the solar system. Heavily-cratered plains alternate with smooth, largely uncratered areas laced with intricate faulting and grooving, forming a spectacular patchwork, and posing all sorts of problems for naturalistic theories. "No one predicted anything looking like Miranda",[10] says one evolutionist astronomer. "How could this patchwork of geologic features wind up on a single, tiny, icy body in orbit about Uranus? Such a small cold moon should not be geologically active."[11] says another.

There are two primary explanations used to explain Miranda's surface. The most popular today is that Miranda's interior was heated by tidal forces. But this requires Miranda to have an eccentric orbit, which it does not have today.

To explain this, researchers are forced to appeal to different conditions in the past, including a much different orbit for Miranda, a previous orbital resonance with Uranus' moon Umbriel, and possibly a resonance with moon Ariel too. But none of these conditions exist today. So this explanation appears

rather contrived. Also, science is supposed to be based on observations. Appealing to different conditions in the past—conditions which are not observed today—raises the question of whether or not this explanation can even be considered scientific.

The second explanation is that Miranda was 'normal' (i.e. as expected by evolution) when formed, and was then repeatedly dismembered by collisions, and reassembled by the mutual gravitational attraction of the resulting pieces. NASA promotes the suggestion that "it has been fractured up to five times during its evolution".[12] Others reject this implausible scenario and dispute whether this moon could even survive *one* collision, let alone five. "Although some sort of collisional disruption appears to be required, it is not obvious that the present terrain, with relief up to 20 km, would survive catastrophic disruption and reassembly."[13]

## Conclusion

Uranus, along with its satellites, poses many unique problems for those who don't want to accept a creation event. In today's scientific age, one is often asked how it is possible to be a Christian in light of 'all that science has discovered'. We see that just the opposite is true—the more we learn, the more we see that indeed, the heavens (along with all the rest of the creation) do indeed declare the glory of God (Psalm 19:1).

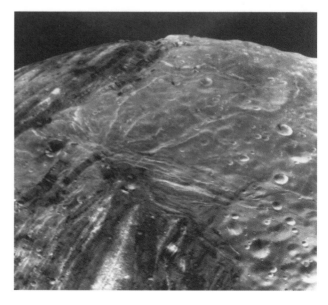

**NASA describes this area as ridges and valleys slapped onto the surface "like mismatched patches on a moth-eaten coat".**

# Uranus Facts

| | |
|---|---|
| Mean distance from the sun | $2{,}872.5 \times 10^6$ km (19.2 AU, i.e. cf. Earth) |
| Mass | $86.813 \times 10^{24}$ kg ($14.54 \times$ Earth) |
| Equatorial radius | 25,559 km ($4 \times$ Earth) |
| Volume | $6{,}833 \times 10^{10}$ km³ ($63 \times$ Earth) |
| Mean density | 1,271 kg/m³ (23.1% Earth) |
| Gravity | 8.87 m/s² (90.5% Earth) |
| Equatorial escape velocity | 21.3 km/sec ($1.9 \times$ Earth) |
| Length of Uranus day | 17.24 hours (72% Earth) |
| Obliquity to orbit (deg) | 97.77° (cf. Earth 23.44°) |
| Inclination of equator (deg) | 82.23° |
| Orbit around sun (i.e. year) | 83.75 Earth years |
| Atmosphere | $H_2$ 82.5%, He 15.2%, $CH_4$ 2.3% |
| Wind speeds | 0–250 m/s (900 km/h) |
| Mean surface temperature | -197° C |
| Number of confirmed moons | 27 |

Source: Uranus Fact Sheet, NASA, updated 19 April 2016

## References and Notes

1. The chapter adapted and updated from Psarris, S., *Creation* **24**(3):38–40, 2002; creation.com/uranus.
2. For technical readers: methane is normally transparent to visible light, because there are no electronic energy changes in this region. But in Uranus and Neptune, the red absorption is due to changes in vibrational energy level. Normally, such changes absorb in the lower-energy infrared region, but methane is so dense that we see the normally weak overtones and combination bands that absorb in the lowest-energy visible light region, red.
3. Its 'geographic' north pole is tilted 82.23° from the ecliptic, but its positive pole is defined by the Right Hand Rule, and its tilt is 97.77°. See discussion in Chapter 4 on Venus.
4. Christiansen, E.H. and Hamblin, W.K., *Exploring the Planets* (2nd edition), Prentice-Hall Inc., New Jersey, p. 405, 1990.
5. For critiques of this idea, see Chapter 8, Sarfati, J., The moon: the light that rules the night; and Oard, M.J., Problems for 'giant impact' origin of moon, *J. Creation* **14**(1):6–7, 2000; creation.com/moonimpact.
6. For an in-depth discussion of this topic see Henry, J., The energy balance of Uranus: implications for special creation, *J. Creation* **15**(3):85–91, 2001; creation.com/uranusenergy.
7. Ref. 4, p. 406.
8. See Humphreys, R., Beyond Neptune: Voyager II supports creation, *Impact* 203, May 1990; icr.org/article/329 and Humphreys, R., The creation of planetary magnetic fields, *Creation Research Society Quarterly* **21**(3):140–149, December 1984; creationresearch.org/crsq/articles/21/21_3/21_3.html.
9. Reversals do not solve the problem. See Chapter 5 box: Sarfati, J., The earth's magnetic field.
10. Taylor, S.R., *Destiny or Chance: our solar system and its place in the cosmos,* Cambridge University Press, Cambridge, p. 86, 1998.
11. Baker, D. and Ratcliff, T., *The 50 Most Extreme Places in Our Solar System*, The Belknap Press of Harvard University Press, p. 204, 2010.
12. See Visiting Miranda, NASA, Last updated 15 July 2015.
13. Taylor, S.R., *Solar System Evolution: A New Perspective*, 2nd ed., Cambridge University Press, p. 240, 2001.

# Chapter 13

# Neptune: monument to Creation

Neptune is the eighth planet from the sun in our solar system. An enormous gas giant, it is about four times the diameter of Earth, 17 times Earth's mass, and 58 times its volume. At about 30 times as far away from the sun as Earth, Neptune takes almost 164 years to orbit the sun once, but its rotation or 'day' is only 16.11 hours. It poses many problems for those who wish to deny creation. Among other things, naturalist theories say that Neptune should not exist!

**Author: Spike Psarris[1]**

Neptune, the furthest from the sun of the eight major planets, was 'discovered' by mathematical prediction. Variations in the orbit of Uranus suggested to French astronomer Le Verrier, and independently to English astronomer John Adams, that there must be another planet beyond it, exerting a gravitational 'pull'. The culprit, Neptune, was observed through a telescope in 1846 by German astronomer Johann Galle, close to the position predicted by both Adams and Le Verrier, and was named after the Roman god of the sea.

Neptune appears as little more than a bluish dot in all but the most powerful telescopes. Its atmosphere is mostly hydrogen, helium, and methane (which absorbs light from the red end of the spectrum, allowing blue light to bounce back out). Neptune's atmosphere is bluer than that of Uranus (which also contains methane); astronomers aren't sure why.

## Neptune's rings

Neptune has six known rings of varying thickness, as confirmed by *Voyager 2* in 1989. They are fainter and darker than those of Saturn, and appear to consist of dust particles in thick and thin regions.

This unevenness means they cannot be billions of years old, since collisions of the ring objects would eventually make the ring very uniform. In fact, NASA admits, "The rings are thought to be relatively young and short-lived."[2]

## Neptune's moons, notably Triton

Neptune has 13 known moons; "a 14th tiny, very dim, moon was discovered in 2013 and awaits official recognition."[2]

The largest moon, Triton, is 2,705 km in diameter (78% of Earth's moon, but slightly larger than the dwarf planets Pluto and Eris), and contradicts standard evolutionary explanation. Its orbit around Neptune is retrograde, i.e. in the opposite direction to the rotation of the planet. So Triton cannot have been formed by the nebular hypothesis, and a capture theory is postulated. Although gravitational capture of a satellite like Triton is extremely unlikely, Triton is only one of many moons for which capture is invoked, in order to explain away contradictions between the evolutionary model's predictions and the observed solar system.

**Relative sizes of the eight planets—all pose problems for evolutionary explanation.**

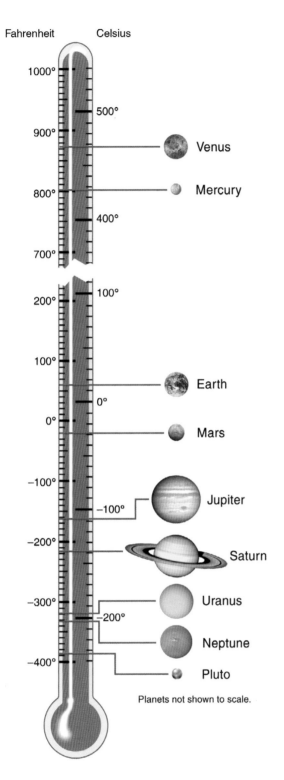

Fahrenheit    Celsius

Venus

Mercury

Earth

Mars

Jupiter

Saturn

Uranus

Neptune

Pluto

Planets not shown to scale.

The various temperatures of the eight planets and Pluto, as provided by the Lunar and Planetary Institute. In general the surface temperature decreases with increasing distance from the sun. Venus is an exception because its dense atmosphere acts as a greenhouse. Mercury rotates very slowly so its day-side temperature is shown. Temperatures for the gas giants are from an atmospheric level equal in pressure to sea level on Earth.

*Top:* Neptune's largest moon, Triton, orbits retrograde, which contradicts the standard evolutionary explanation. Although one of the coldest moons in the solar system, it has numerous geysers, indicating youth not age.
*Bottom:* Composite illustration of Neptune as seen from its moon, Triton. Notice the smooth surface of Triton and lack of impact craters.

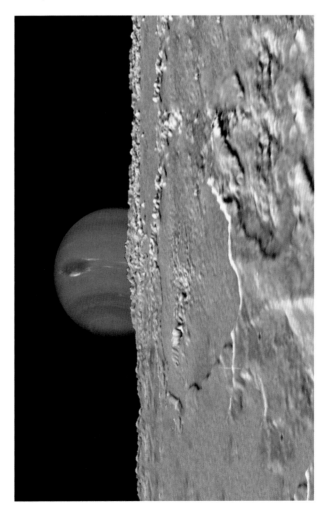

Triton's orbit around Neptune is nearly a perfect circle, and its rotation is tidally locked so that it keeps one face oriented toward its planet at all times.

Triton has a sparsely cratered surface with smooth volcanic plains, mounds and round pits formed by icy lava flows. Triton's surface is one of the coldest in the solar system, -235 °C,[3] and is covered with frozen nitrogen condensed from its atmosphere. Despite this, *Voyager 2* observed numerous geysers spewing material (believed to be nitrogen liquid or gas) upward more than 8 km. These factors all indicate Triton is young, not old.

## Problems for naturalism

Neptune poses many problems for those who wish to deny creation. Among other things, naturalistic theories say that Neptune shouldn't exist!

Our best photographs and measurements of Neptune and its moons were taken by the *Voyager 2* spacecraft, which flew by the planet in August 1989. Many of these measurements greatly surprised evolutionary scientists. They had assumed Neptune would be a cold, inactive place, but it is not.

Neptune has winds that rage at almost 2,100 km/h (1,300 mph), i.e. supersonic, and the strongest measured in the solar system. In 1989, *Voyager 2* imaged two large spots in the southern hemisphere, thought to have been enormous spinning atmospheric storms. The larger one, dubbed 'Great Dark Spot', measured 13,000 × 6,600 km, and was about the diameter of Earth and similar to Jupiter's Great Red Spot. When the *Hubble Space Telescope* viewed the planet in 1994 these two spots had disappeared (unlike Jupiter's which has lasted for hundreds of years). However, another smaller one then appeared in the northern hemisphere. Neptune is a dynamic, ever-changing place.

Neptune is nowhere near as cold as evolutionary theory predicts. Instead, it actually *generates* heat, radiating into space over twice the energy it receives from the sun. This fits the Creation model very well, as a young Neptune could easily still be cooling off a few thousand years after its creation. However, this does not fit the evolutionary long-age model, as many evolutionists have acknowledged.[4] Overall, with its raging winds, dynamic atmosphere, and heat generation, Neptune appears quite young.

## Magnetic field problems

The *Voyager 2* measurements of Neptune's magnetic field also upset evolutionary theories. Three years earlier, *Voyager 2* had flown by the planet Uranus, discovering that Uranus's magnetic field is tilted relative to the planet's spin axis, and offset from the planet's centre. Both these characteristics contradict the evolutionary 'dynamo' model of planetary magnetism (this hypothetical 'self-generating' mechanism for sustaining a magnetic field is essential for long-agers, because without some renewal such fields decay away to nothing in only a few thousand years).

So evolutionists consoled themselves by speculating

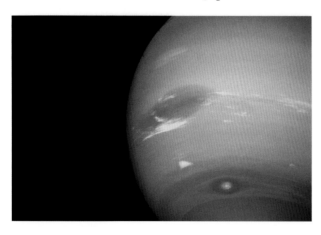

In 1989, *Voyager 2* captured this image of two huge spinning storms in Neptune's southern atmosphere. By 1994 they had both disappeared.

Cirrus clouds on Neptune are thought to be formed from methane ice crystals, as the melting points and boiling points of hydrogen and helium are much lower than the frigid temperatures of Neptune and even Triton.

that perhaps *Voyager 2* "had caught the Uranus field in the middle of a reversal (when the magnetic north and south poles switch places)."[5] This is very unlikely, but not necessarily impossible. But then *Voyager 2* flew by Neptune and discovered that its field was tilted and offset, too. Scientists were forced to concede that "it seems that the possibility of finding two planets both experiencing magnetic polarity reversals is small."[5] Of course, creationists are not bound to dynamo theories, or to millions of years. Creationist astrophysicist Dr Russell Humphreys was able to predict the magnetic characteristics of Uranus and Neptune (before *Voyager 2* measured them) with much more success than the evolutionists, by assuming (based on the Bible) that the planets began as masses of water (Genesis 1:2; 2 Peter 3:5) and that creation occurred roughly 6,000 years ago.[6]

## Neptune shouldn't exist!

We know from the Bible that Neptune was created on Day 4 along with the other "lights in the heavens". Evolutionary scientists (and 'long-age creationists') scoff at this history, believing instead that the solar system formed from an enormous cloud of gas and dust. Over postulated millions of years, the dust allegedly clumped together into rocks, these rocks clumped together into bigger rocks, and eventually there were enormous rocks ('planetesimals') flying around, which stuck together and became planets. The gas giants are supposed to have formed at the outer reaches of the solar system because it was cold enough there for the components to condense as ice, making the growing planetoid massive enough to attract gas.

Unfortunately for evolutionists, Neptune doesn't fit that model. An article in the (pro-evolution) *Astronomy* magazine explained it this way:

"Pssst ... astronomers who model the formation of the solar system have kept a dirty little secret: Uranus and Neptune don't exist. Or at least computer simulations have never explained how planets as big as the two gas giants could form so far from the sun. Bodies orbited so slowly in the outer parts of the sun's protoplanetary disk that the slow process of gravitational accretion would need more time than the age of the solar system to form bodies with 14.5 and 17.1 times the mass of Earth."[7]

In evolutionary models of the solar system, the farther you are from the middle of the alleged gas/dust cloud (where the sun is today), the longer the planet-formation procedure requires. Neptune and Uranus are too far out to have formed according to this process, even over the supposed 4.5-billion-year age assigned to the solar system. One evolutionist astronomer wryly commented:

"What is clear is that simple banging together of planetesimals to construct planets takes too long in this remote outer part of the solar system. The time needed exceeds the age of the solar system. We see Uranus and Neptune, but the modest requirement that these planets exist has not been met by this model."[8]

How much more time is needed? Another (evolutionary) book explains:

"When Safronov's theory [of planet formation] was applied to the conditions given by the SNT [Solar Nebula Theory], it was found that the time for forming the Earth was a few million years, for Jupiter about 250 million years and for Neptune about 10 billion years—twice the age of the Solar System."[9]

So even if the solar system really were 4.5 billion years old, as evolutionists say, we would still be 5.5 billion years short of the time necessary for Uranus and Neptune to have formed by themselves.[10] This is why *Astronomy* magazine said that, according to evolution, "Uranus and Neptune don't exist."[7]

Safronov published these calculations in 1972. So, this problem has been recognized for well over 40 years. Why then do the textbooks and popular media so confidently proclaim that we 'know' for certain that the solar system formed by itself over thousands of millions of years? Shouldn't the 'fact' that some of the planets 'don't exist' cause some doubt?

Of course, creationists are not alone in noticing the absurdity of this situation. Many evolutionists have been trying to come up with a solution.

"Attempts have been made to rescue the theory of planetesimal aggregation by considering factors that might speed up the process but these have not been very convincing. Even postulating unsupportable extreme conditions in the solar nebula, the problem of the outer planets cannot be solved."[9]

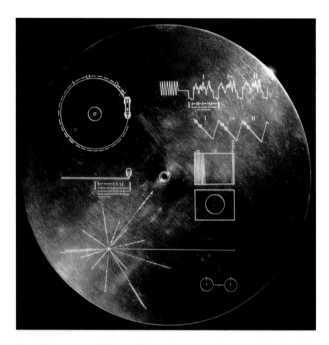

*Top*: **The cover of the golden phonograph record carried by the *Voyager* spacecraft, designed to accommodate evolutionary belief by informing any aliens encountered about us.** *Bottom*: **The golden record's location on *Voyager* (middle-bottom-left).**

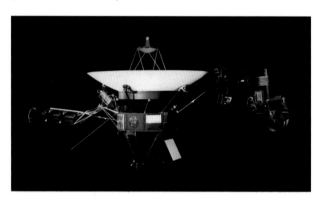

The *Astronomy* article mentioned above then considers the 'migration' idea (see Chapter 1 for more on this theory):

"… Edward Thommes and Martin Duncan of Queens University in Ontario and Hal Levison of the Southwest Research Institute in Colorado report a possible way to get around the problem. Maybe Uranus and Neptune began forming closer to the sun, where there was more material to make giant planets and timescales are much shorter …"[7]

before concluding pessimistically:

"'It's clear that our level of sophistication of studying planet formation is relatively primitive,' concedes Duncan. But he adds, 'So far it's been very difficult for anybody to come up with a scenario that actually produces Uranus and Neptune.'"[7]

### 'Once upon a time …!'

Here we see the true heart of the matter. The ultimate goal of the evolutionist is to 'come up with a scenario' of how the universe formed by itself, without a Creator. Sadly, they often seem to believe that the mere act of making up such a story proves that it all actually happened that way. It doesn't even have to be a *good* story. Indeed, in this article we've seen that, instead of acknowledging their Creator, evolutionists would rather cling to a story that *denies the existence of the very objects that it's supposed to explain.*

Ultimately, it really doesn't matter if somebody eventually is able to 'come up with a scenario' about the formation of Neptune. Our outlook on life should not depend on whether or not someone has been able to concoct a good story. For thousands of years, sinful man has been shaking his fist at God, and inventing fables about how we all got here, without a Creator. Today, the stories are more sophisticated, and often backed up with impressive-seeming computer simulations, but it's really the same thing as before.

It is assumed that life began elsewhere in space without a Creator. Both the NASA *Voyager 1* and *Voyager 2* spacecraft carried a golden phonograph record (designed by a committee chaired by atheist Carl Sagan) to inform any of their imagined aliens encountered, about life on Earth. That any such ETs had a phonograph player operating at the designated 16⅔ revs per minute was apparently taken for granted.

### Conclusion

The 'gas and dust' story is about as good as evolutionary models get—it's been around in various forms for hundreds of years,[11] hundreds of very intelligent people have worked on various aspects of it, and almost all evolutionary astronomers today believe it. Yet even though this 'well-proven' model pretends to explain the origin of the planets, it (embarrassingly enough) still predicts that some of those planets can't exist.

Why then would we want to put our faith in these sorts of fables, invented by sinful man? Far better to place our faith in the living Word of God, the Bible. Its historicity, accuracy and reliability are above reproach!

# Neptune Facts

| | |
|---|---|
| Mean distance from the sun | $4{,}495 \times 10^6$ km (30 AU, i.e. cf. Earth) |
| Mass | $102.4 \times 10^{24}$ kg (17.15 × Earth) |
| Equatorial radius | 24,764 km (3.88 × Earth) |
| Mean density | 1,638 kg/m³ (29.7% Earth) |
| Gravity | 11.15 m/s² (1.14 × Earth) |
| Equatorial escape velocity | 23.5 km/s (2.1 × Earth) |
| Length of Neptune day | 16.11 hours (67% Earth) |
| Orbit around sun (i.e. year) | 163.73 Earth days |
| Mean surface temperature | -201° C |
| Atmosphere | $H_2$ 80.0%, He 19.0%, $CH_4$ 1.5% Traces HD, $C_2H_6$ |

Source: Neptune Fact Sheet, NASA, updated 19 April 2016

## References and Notes

1. This chapter adapted and updated from Psarris, S., *Creation* **25**(1):22–24, 2003; creation.com/neptune-monument-to-creation.
2. As per NASA, solarsystem.nasa.gov/planets/neptune/indepth, accessed April 23, 2016.
3. Pluto is about the same temperature; see Chapter 14.
4. For more in depth on this topic, see Samec, R., The age of the jovian planets, *J. Creation* **14**(1):3–4, 2000; creation.com/jupiter and Henry, J., The energy balance of Uranus: implications for special creation, *J. Creation* **15**(3):85–91, 2001; creation.com/uranusenergy.
5. Christiansen, E.H. and Hamblin, W.K., *Exploring the Planets*, 2nd Edition, Prentice-Hall Inc., New Jersey, p. 424, 1990.
6. See Humphreys, R., Beyond Neptune: Voyager II supports creation, *Impact* 203, 1990; icr.org/article/329 and Humphreys, R., The creation of planetary magnetic fields, *Creation Research Society Quarterly* **21**(3):140–149, 1984; creationresearch.org/crsq/articles/21/21_3/21_3.html. His published predictions in 1984 on the field strength were 100,000 times greater than the evolutionary ones, and his article said it would be a good test of his theory. The results were squarely in the middle of Humphreys' prediction.

7. Robert Naeye, Birth of Uranus and Neptune, *Astronomy* **28**(4):30, April 2000.
8. Taylor, S.R., *Destiny or Chance: our solar system and its place in the cosmos*, Cambridge University Press, Cambridge, p. 73, 1998. A nearly identical statement appears in Taylor, S.R., *Solar System Evolution: A New Perspective*, Cambridge University Press, 2nd ed., p. 206, 2001.
9. Woolfson, M.M., *On The Origins of Planets by Means of Natural Simple Processes*, Imperial College Press, p. xli, 2011.
10. Actually, the problem is even worse than it appears; we are not only lacking enough time to form Neptune, but the planetesimals, etc. from which to build it aren't around any more. Notice that the models require that the planetesimals would have dissipated long ago (to explain the lack of them today), but simultaneously need them around for thousands of millions of years, in order to eventually build Neptune.
11. The first nebular hypothesis is usually attributed to Pierre Laplace in 1796, although Immanuel Kant had proposed a similar idea 40 years earlier. And 20 years before that, the mystic Emmanuel Swedenborg claimed he got a similar idea from a séance!

# Chapter 14

# Pluto and other dwarf planets

Pluto was first sighted by astronomer Clyde Tombaugh (1906–1997) in February 1930 from the Lowell Observatory in Arizona. He did this by comparing photographs of stars taken two weeks apart to see if any objects had shifted their position. One object qualified, and being beyond Neptune it was acclaimed the ninth planet. The name Pluto was suggested by 11-year-old English school-girl Venetia Burney (1918–2009), because in Greek mythology Pluto was the ruler of the underworld, a cold dark place that sunlight did not reach. The first two letters are also Lowell's initials.

**Authors: Russell Grigg and Tas Walker[1]**

However, Lowell had grossly over-estimated the size of his extra planet. He thought it would be six times more massive than Earth, but we now know it is a little less than 1/5th of the diameter of Earth, and about 1/450th of Earth's mass.

Then, from 1992 on, astronomers discovered many objects orbiting the sun in the same area as Pluto, i.e. beyond Neptune in a space called the Kuiper Belt.[2] Some of these objects rivalled Pluto in size. In 2005, astronomers discovered Eris, which has a mass 27% more than Pluto's, although it is slightly smaller in volume. So this was even suggested as a tenth planet, although some astronomers considered this discovery was a good reason to reclassify Pluto as a minor planet.

Finally, in August 2006, the International Astronomical Union (IAU) somewhat controversially demoted Pluto from being the ninth planet, and classified it and Eris in a new category of solar-system objects called 'dwarf planets'.

These are objects that have sufficient size/mass for their gravity to pull them into a near-spherical shape, but are too small to clear their orbit of smaller objects. Planets, on the other hand, gravitationally pull some of the objects in their orbit into themselves, and fling others permanently out of the way. Smaller bodies, such as asteroids, usually have an irregular shape.

The IAU currently has named five dwarf planets: Pluto, Eris, Makemake, Haumea, and Ceres. It is thought that several hundred other objects in the Kuiper Belt qualify as dwarf planets, and perhaps even thousands more outside the Kuiper Belt. In 2008, the IAU decided on the title 'plutoid' for Pluto and other dwarf planets that orbit the sun beyond Neptune, i.e. 'trans-Neptunian objects'. The dwarf planet Ceres is not a plutoid because it orbits the sun in the asteroid belt between Mars and Jupiter. But the other four dwarf planets are.

### Some facts about the current dwarf planets

| Dwarf Planet | Equatorial diameter | Orbital period |
| --- | --- | --- |
| Pluto | 2,370 km | 248 years |
| Eris | 2,325 | 560 |
| Makemake | 1,500 | 310 |
| Haumea | 1,150 | 285 |
| Ceres | 975 | 4.6 |

# CRATERLESS PLAIN

The smooth surface and lack of craters on Pluto's Sputnik Planum (Sputnik Plain) are strong evidence that Pluto is young

## The real Pluto

On 14 July 2015, the NASA spacecraft *New Horizons* flew past Pluto and its moons, after a 9½-year, 4.8-billion–km (3-billion–mile) journey from Earth. The images sent back to Earth show a multi-coloured world with an astonishing range of features, including mountains that appear to be made of water ice, a huge flat area with no impact craters at all, other areas with a few

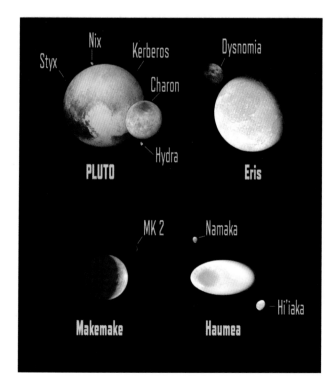

The four trans-Neptunian objects (TNOs), Pluto, Eris, Makemake, and Haumea, recognised by the International Astronomy Union as being plutoids, with their moons.

Pluto and its moon, Charon, compared in size with planet Earth and its moon.

impact craters, dark areas yet to be identified, and blue skies indicating an atmosphere.

Many of these features have been described as 'puzzling' because, contrary to evolutionists' long-age expectations, they show that Pluto 'looks young'. This is because the features indicated that it had to have been recently geologically active. But this should not be possible for an object of Pluto's small size. Smaller objects cool off more rapidly, and if the solar system really were 4.5 billion years old, Pluto would have been 'stone cold dead' long ago.

## Pluto's mountains of ice

Pluto has long been believed to have a rocky core, consistent with its overall density plus evolutionary ideas of how the planets formed (see Chapter 1). It is now thought that the core is surrounded by water ice and frozen nitrogen, together with an abundance of frozen methane, with frozen carbon monoxide coating the surface. A mountain range 3.35 km (2.1 miles) high (rivalling the North American Rockies), and another 1.6 km (1 mile) high, appear to be made of water ice. At Pluto's frigid temperature of –235° C (–390° F), ice is as hard as rock,[3] and so it would have taken a lot of energy for them to have been thrust up so high.

These two areas have been named Norgay Montes and Hillary Montes respectively, in honour of Nepalese Sherpa Tenzing Norgay and New Zealander Edmund Hillary, who together made the first ascent of Mt Everest in 1953. Two other mountain areas on Pluto look somewhat similar to volcanoes on Earth, leading scientists to suggest that in their past these Pluto mountains may have ejected a slurry of water ice, with liquid nitrogen, ammonia, or methane,[4] rather than molten rock as on Earth.

## Pluto's virgin 'heart'

Adjacent to these mountain ranges is a flat heart-shaped feature dubbed 'Tombaugh Regio' (after Clyde Tombaugh), about 1,600 km (1,000 miles) wide. In the centre-left or western lobe of this 'heart'-land is an area dubbed 'Sputnik Planum' (after Earth's first artificial satellite), thought to be a lake of frozen nitrogen. It is completely unblemished by meteorite impacts. This has produced expressions of amazement from NASA scientists, with opinions ranging from: "a vast craterless plain that appears to be no more than 100 million years old",[5] to "This could be only a week old, for all we know."[6]

## Pluto's atmosphere

Pluto has a thin hazy atmosphere that appears to extend out about 1,600 km (1,000 miles). It consists of ~98% nitrogen (cf. 78% on Earth), with small amounts of methane, and carbon monoxide. The haze was shown as a blue ring surrounding Pluto after *New Horizons* had passed and then 'looked back' to photograph the sun's light passing through Pluto's atmosphere as an eclipse. The blue colour results from the scattering of sunlight by small air particles, which on Earth are mostly nitrogen molecules.

Pluto's atmosphere also contains methane, and it is thought that cosmic rays interact with methane to form reddish hydrocarbon molecules called tholins, and that these coalesce to fall to Pluto's surface and impart the red colours there.[7]

The low gravity of Pluto (~7% of Earth's) allows hundreds of tonnes of Pluto's atmospheric nitrogen to escape into space each hour, leading scientists to speculate that the nitrogen may be coming from relatively recent geological activity within Pluto itself.[8]

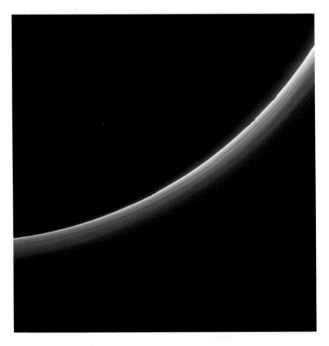

**Pluto's atmosphere backlit by the sun looks blue, thought to be caused by tiny particles in the atmosphere scattering the sunlight.**

## Pluto's moons

Pluto has five known moons. The largest and closest to Pluto is Charon. It is 1,207 km (750 miles) in diameter, about half the size of Pluto (2,374 km, 1,475 miles), and as such is the largest satellite relative to its planet in the solar system. Its mean distance from Pluto is just 19,600 km (12,180 miles). For comparison, Earth's moon is an average of 384,400 km (238,855 miles) away from us. Because of their closeness, Pluto and Charon orbit a mutual centre of mass between them, a point in space known as a barycentre, which in turn orbits the sun. This is why Pluto appears to 'wobble' in space when viewed from Earth.

*New Horizons* images show Charon has a surface canyon that is at least four times longer than the USA's Grand Canyon and in places twice as deep. Much of Charon is free of impact craters, with ridges and grooves that suggest recent geological activity, unlike what many scientists expected.

Pluto and Charon orbit each other approximately every 6.4 days. They are 'locked' to one another by gravitational attraction, so each keeps the same face towards the other. However, it is thought that the gravitational tidal forces each imposes on the other are not strong enough to cause internal ices to melt and erupt. So this precludes any heating effects between the two. It is a case of mutual tidal locking, in contrast to that of the earth and the moon, where our moon always shows the same face to Earth, but not vice versa.

Charon looks young, too! According to NASA: "Mission scientists are surprised by the apparent lack of craters on Charon. South of the moon's equator … relatively few craters are visible, indicating a relatively young surface that has been reshaped by geologic activity."[9] But if Pluto's persistent activity at its small size is a puzzle for long-agers, Charon, at only one-eighth of Pluto's volume, significantly deepens the mystery. In an 'old' system, it should have been geologically 'dead' long before Pluto, even.

The other four moons of Pluto beyond Charon are, from closest to furthest out, Styx, Nix, Kerberos, and Hydra. They all orbit Pluto anticlockwise, and they all rotate at different speeds, like spinning tops, as they orbit. Charon rotates once per lap because it is gravitationally locked to Pluto, Styx rotates 6.22 times,

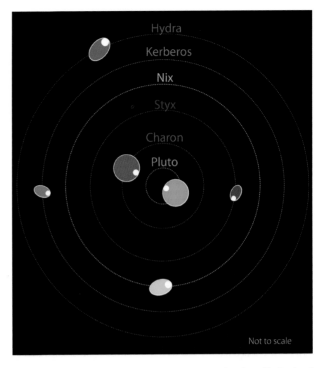

Only one of Pluto's moons, Charon, is gravitationally locked to Pluto. The other four moons rotate like spinning tops, with Nix rotating backwards and on its side. All of this chaos contradicts the evolutionary hypothesis.

Nix 13.6 times, Kerberos 6.04 times, and Hydra rotates an amazing 88.9 times during each 38.2 day orbit or once every 10.3 hours.[10] Nix rotates retrograde, i.e. backwards or clockwise against its anti-clockwise orbit. Also Nix is tilted on its axis by 132 degrees. Such 'chaos' is contrary to the nebular hypothesis.

## Pluto and its moons contradict the nebular hypothesis

Pluto is a problem for the nebular hypothesis, i.e. the theory that our solar system supposedly formed from a primeval cloud of gas and dust 4.5 billion years ago, all rotating in the same direction.

1.  Pluto does not orbit in the same plane as the eight planets (i.e., the ecliptic) but at an angle of 17°.
2.  Pluto's axis of rotation is not perpendicular to its orbital plane but is tilted so that one pole points almost directly at the sun.
3.  Pluto's orbit is not circular but highly elliptical. In fact, for 20 of the 248 Earth years its orbit takes, it actually comes closer to the sun than Neptune, e.g. between 7 February 1979 and 11 February 1999.
4.  Pluto's five moons all rotate at different speeds as

they orbit Pluto, and one, Nix, rotates backwards against its orbit.

5.  Evidence of persistent geological activity on Pluto and its moons challenges the idea of billions of years.

### How old is Pluto?

Counting impact craters is one method scientists use to assign relative ages—the more craters, the longer it could have taken to form them (that is, assuming the meteors and asteroids that formed the craters didn't all arrive in showers). NASA scientists claim to have counted over 1,000 impact craters on Pluto that vary greatly in size and appearance, leading them to claim that Pluto must be billions of years old. However, the lack of craters on the heart-shaped area called Sputnik Planum is a huge problem for the evolutionary theory that the solar system formed 4.5 billion years ago. So scientists have suggested that the craterless plain has been renewed by a heat source; but if so, what?

Not from Pluto's original formation. Pluto is so small that any primordial heat would have dissipated into space long ago, if it is billions of years old. Since it orbits ~6 billion km (~4 billion miles) from the sun, its temperature is –235° C (–390° F). This is below the freezing point of all

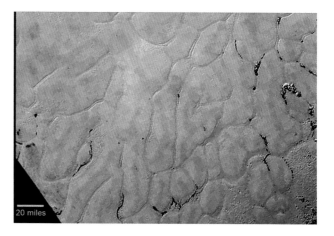

**Many features of Pluto that puzzle evolutionists, such as this craterless plane, are resolved when the long-age interpretation is replaced by a short age for the planet.**

gases, except neon, hydrogen and helium.

The density of Pluto (38% of Earth's) is too small to allow for long-lived radioactive elements to provide heat for billions of years.

Pluto is not near enough to any other object large enough to cause tidal effects within Pluto and so raise its temperature.

If the interior of Pluto were warm enough to erode the surface then the mountains of ice on Pluto should have melted long ago.

**An artist's concept of *New Horizons* investigating Pluto.**

# Pluto Facts

| | |
|---|---|
| Mean distance from the sun | $5906.4 \times 10^6$ km (39.5 AU, i.e. cf. Earth) |
| Mass | $0.013 \times 10^{24}$ (0.22% Earth) |
| Equatorial radius | 1,187 km (18.6% Earth) |
| Mean density | 1,860 kg/m$^3$ (33.7% Earth) |
| Gravity | 0.62 m/s$^2$ (6.3% Earth) |
| Equatorial escape velocity | 1.21 km/s (10.8% Earth) |
| Length of Pluto day | 153.28 hours (6.39 × Earth) |
| Obliquity to orbit | 122.53º |
| Inclination of equator | 57.47º |
| Atmosphere | Methane, nitrogen, hydrocarbons |
| Number of moons | 5 |

Source: Pluto Fact Sheet, NASA, updated 19 April 2016.

The lack of impact craters on a huge area of Pluto and on Charon speaks against a billions-of-years timeframe.

## Conclusion

Problems associated with the appearance and activity of Pluto dissolve when the evolutionary assumption of an age of billions of years for it is dropped. In a solar system only several thousand years old, energy could still be dissipating since creation. *New Horizons* has provided evidence that the solar system cannot be billions of years old—only thousands, as the Bible indicates.

## References and Notes

1. This chapter adapted and updated from Walker, T., *Creation* **31**(2):54–55, 2009; creation.com/pluto-lesson; and Grigg, R., Pluto: Flyby photos show it looks young, *Creation* **38**(3):46–49, 2016.
2. The Kuiper Belt extends from about 30 to 55 astronomical units (compared to Earth which is one astronomical unit, or AU, from the sun). Many small solar-system objects in it are composed mostly of frozen chemicals such as water, nitrogen, ammonia, and methane.
3. Ice has long been known to become harder as the temperature is lowered. Even at a far less frigid temperature of -78.5° C, the sublimation point of dry ice ($CO_2$), ice is as hard as orthoclase feldspar and "hard enough to abrade limestone, shale, and many other common rocks, even including some igneous masses," Blackwelder, E., The hardness of ice: *American Journal of Science* **238**:61–62, 1940; cf. Butkevich T.R., Hardness of single ice crystals, *American Mineralogist* **43**:48–57, 1958.
4. Volcanoes that eject such volatiles are called cryovolcanoes.
5. NASA News, 18 July, 2015, Frozen Plains in the Heart of Pluto's 'Heart'.
6. Jeffrey Moore, Leader of the New Horizons Geology, Geophysics and Imaging Team at NASA's Ames Research Center, California, NASA, speaking at a NASA headquarters press conference in Washington DC, as reported by Jacob Aron, *New Scientist* Daily News 17 July 2015, New Horizons team baffled by discovery of icy plains on Pluto; and by Nadia Drake, *National Geographic* News 17 July 2015, New Pluto Photos Show 'Astoundingly Amazing' Landscape; as well as reported by numerous other periodicals and newspapers worldwide.
7. NASA/Johns Hopkins University Applied Physics Laboratory/ Southwest Research Institute, 3 July 2015, The 'Other' Red Planet.
8. NASA News, August 10 2015, Atmospheric Escape and Flowing $N_2$ Ice Glaciers—what Resupplies Pluto's Nitrogen?
9. NASA July 16, 2015, Charon's Surprising, Youthful and Varied Terrain.
10. Data posted by Emily Lakdawalla from 47th Annual Meeting of the American Astronomical Society's Division for Planetary Sciences, Pluto's small moons Styx, Nix, Kerberos, and Hydra [updated], The Planetary Society, 25 November 2015.

# Chapter 15

# Comets: portents of doom or indicators of youth?

Comets have long fascinated (and often horrified) mankind. They seem to come from nowhere, and disappear just as suddenly. Their tails seem to dwarf other heavenly bodies. People viewed them as portents of disaster, and indeed a comet appeared about the time of the futile Jewish revolt against the Romans in AD 66 which ended in the destruction of Jerusalem in AD 70; and also before the Battle of Hastings in 1066. There are many historical records of comet sightings.

**Author: Jonathan Sarfati**[1]

Perhaps the most famous such comet sighting is the one recorded in the Bayeux Tapestry, an embroidered cloth about 70 m (230 ft) long and 0.5 m (20 in) tall made in England in the 1070s and then hung in Bayeux Cathedral, France. It depicts the events leading up to and including the Battle of Hastings on 14 October 1066, where the Duke of Normandy, William (the Conqueror), defeated the last Saxon King, Harold II. The tapestry was commissioned by Odo, Bishop of Bayeux and Earl of Kent, William's maternal half-brother. In one frame, several people are shown looking in alarm at the comet depicted in the sky.

**A frame from the Bayeux Tapestry showing the words, *'Isti mirant stella'*, Latin for 'They wondered at a star', and a stylized picture of what we now know was the AD 1066 appearance of Halley's Comet. At the time, the *Anglo-Saxon Chronicle* stated, "… all over England there was seen in the sky such a sign as men had never seen before."**

## Triumph of biblical worldview over astrological superstition

Many people have attempted or claimed to tell fortunes from the heavenly bodies (astrology); instead we should gain information from their Creator, in His written Word, the Bible. It was the biblical worldview which led to the science that explained comets. The Bible teaches that the universe was made by a God of order (1 Corinthians 14:33), who gave mankind dominion over creation (Genesis 1:26–28). Historians of science, regardless of their own religious faith, from Christians to atheists, acknowledge the vital importance of the Christian worldview in the rise of modern experimental science.

For instance, Johannes Kepler (1571–1630) formulated the laws of planetary motion. Kepler calculated a creation date of 3992 BC, even younger than the famous date of 4004 BC calculated by his contemporary, Archbishop James Ussher (1581–1656). Then Isaac Newton (1643–1727), widely regarded as the greatest scientist of all time, developed the laws of motion, gravity and calculus. But he wrote more on biblical history than he did on science, and vigorously defended Ussher's chronology.[2]

Newton's friend Edmond Halley (1656–1742) applied these laws to about 25 observed comets and showed that they followed predictable paths. In particular, he noticed that a comet he observed in 1682 followed an orbit very much like that of similar comets seen in 1531 and 1607. So he realized that it was really the same comet reappearing at intervals—now averaging 76 years. This was also the comet that appeared in 1066, AD 66, and also 12 BC, a few years before Christ was born.[3] When he successfully predicted that the comet would appear in a particular year (after his death), this was seen as a great triumph for Newton's theories, and the comet was deservedly named after Halley.

## Origin of comets

The Word of the Creator of the comets, which inspired the development of the science that demystified them, also tells us when He made them. In Genesis 1:14–19, He told us that He made the Sun, Moon and stars on Day 4 of Creation Week, which was about 4000 BC, as Kepler and Newton realized. Since the Hebrew word for

star refers to any bright heavenly object, it presumably includes comets as well.

The features of comets make perfect sense in a biblical timescale, but are a huge problem for evolution and billions of years. Because all age indicators work on assumptions, the argument here is not claimed as 'proof' of a 'young' solar system. Because of the reliable eyewitness account of the Creator in the Bible, the young age is accepted. And this article, among many others,[4] shows that even under the evolutionists' own assumptions, there are huge problems for their timescale.

## What are comets?

Comets are 'dirty snowballs' (or 'dirty icebergs'[5,6]) that revolve around the sun in highly elliptical orbits. They are usually a few km across, but Halley's is about 10 km (6 miles). Comet Hale-Bopp, seen in 1997, at about 40 km (25 miles) is one of the largest comets known. They contain dust and 'ice', which is not just frozen water, but also frozen ammonia, methane and carbon dioxide. Some may also contain a nucleus of hard rock, but it is only the volatiles that form the tails.

Space probes that have visited comets include *Stardust*, *Giotto*, *Deep Impact*, and *Philae*. These missions revealed that comets contain copious dust,

**Comet Hale-Bopp is one of the largest comets known.**

**An artist's impression of the robotic space probe *Stardust* entering the tail of comet Wild 2 to collect dust samples to bring them to Earth for analysis.**

**An artificially coloured composite image of the nucleus of comet Wild 2 superimposed on an image of jets of material leaving the comet.**

comprised of high-temperature minerals, confounding evolutionary expectations of pristine ice with just a dash of cold-origin dust. Scientists were forced by their evolutionary assumptions to postulate wildly improbable processes for getting material from the hot inner solar system out to the cold outer reaches where they believe the comets formed.

In 1992, *Giotti* performed the closest ever comet flyby when it came within 200 km of comet Grigg–Skjellerup,[7] but unfortunately dust-grain impact damage to the space probe's camera prevented pictures being taken.

**An artist's rendering of the *Giotto* space probe approaching a comet.**

## How comets shine—problem for long-agers

When comets approach the sun, some of the ice and frozen gases vapourize and begin to form a coma (atmosphere) around the nucleus at a distance of about 5 AU from the sun (1 AU = ~150 million km). This coma grows to be typically 10,000–100,000 km (rarely up to one million km) wide. When the comet is about 1 AU from the sun, the solar wind (charged particles radiating from the sun) pushes a gas tail (ions or electrically charged atoms of the comet) directly away from the sun. The outflowing gases also drag small dust grains with them, and solar radiation causes these dust particles to form a second tail that curves gently away from the sun and backwards towards the orbit. As the

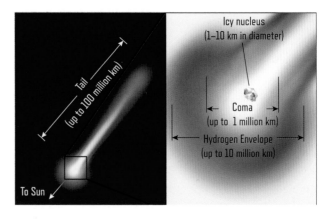

**Anatomy of a comet. A small icy core is the fuel for a massive and often spectacular main tail. Eventually, such a nucleus will lose its mass as it orbits the sun and will cease to exist as such. The short life of comets is testimony to the short age of the solar system and its planets.**

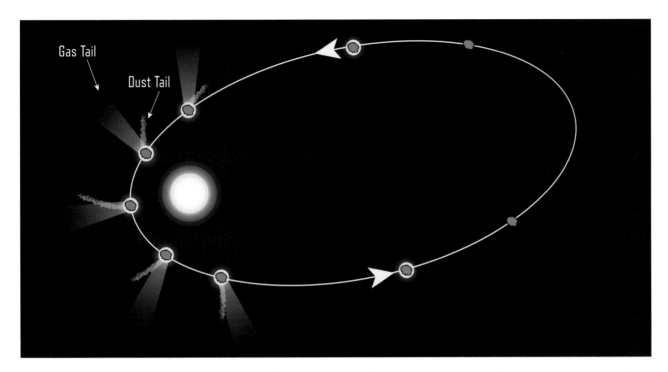

**As a comet approaches the sun, a stream of ions forms a plasma tail pointing directly away from the sun; a stream of dust particles forms a second tail that curves back towards the orbit. As the comet recedes from the sun, tails and coma disappear.**

comet continues on its orbit, solar heating diminishes, and the tails and coma disappear when the comet is between 3 and 5 AU away from the sun.

The coma and tails have a very low density—even the best vacuums produced in laboratories are denser. Earth passed through a tail of Halley's comet in 1910, and it was hardly noticeable. But comets reflect the sun's light very strongly, which can make them very spectacular when they are close to both the sun and Earth. The appearance like a hairy star is responsible for the term 'comet', from the Greek word κομήτης *comētēs* (long-haired).

This means that the comet is slowly being destroyed every time it comes close to the sun. In fact, many comets have been observed to become much dimmer in later passes. Even Halley's comet was brighter in the past.[8] Also, comets are in danger of being captured by planets, like Comet Shoemaker–Levy 9 crashing into Jupiter in 1994 (for a description of this event and images, see Chapter 10), or comets can be ejected from the solar system. A direct hit on Earth is unlikely, but could be disastrous because of the comet's huge kinetic (motion) energy. Such a hit might have been responsible for the 1908 Tunguska event, in which the explosion of an object from space flattened

2,000 km² (770 sq. miles) of forest—fortunately unpopulated. But without a direct impact, comets are far too small to inflict even the tiniest damage, despite sensationalist claims about Comet Elenin in 2011.[9]

The problem for evolutionists is that given the observed rate of loss and maximum periods, comets could not have been orbiting the sun for the alleged billions of years.[10,11]

## Two groups of comets

Comets are divided into two groups: short-period (<200 years) comets, such as Halley's (76 years); and long-period (>200 years) comets. But the comets from the two groups seem essentially the same in size and composition. Short-period ones normally orbit in the same direction as the planets (prograde) and in almost the same plane (ecliptic); long-period comets can orbit in either direction (prograde or retrograde) and in almost any plane. One exception is Halley's, which has retrograde motion to Earth and a highly inclined orbit. Some astronomers suggest that it was once a long-period comet, and strong gravity from a planet dramatically shrunk its orbit, and thus the period. Accordingly, long-period and Halley-type comets are grouped together and called 'nearly isotropic comets' (NICs).

The highest period of a stable orbit would be about four million years if the maximum possible aphelion (furthest distance of an orbiting satellite from the sun) were 50,000 AU.[12] This is 20% of the distance to the nearest star, so there's a fair chance other stars could release the comet from the sun's grip.[13]

However, even with this long orbit, such a comet would still have made 1,200 trips around the sun if the solar system were 4.5 billion years old. Thus, it would have been extinguished long ago. The problem is even worse with short-period comets.

## Hypothetical sources

The only solution for evolutionists is hypothetical sources to replenish the supply of comets:

### *Oort cloud*

The best-known hypothetical source is the Oort cloud, after the Dutch astronomer Jan Hendrik Oort (1900–1992) who proposed it in 1950. This is allegedly a spherical cloud of comets extending as far as three light-years from the sun. It is proposed as a source of long-period comets. Passing stars, gas clouds and galactic tides are supposed to be able to knock comets from the Oort cloud into orbits entering the inner solar system. But there are several problems:

**No observational support:**[14] The Oort cloud has never been observed—indeed evolutionists admit that it is impossible to see it. Therefore it's doubtful that the Oort Cloud should be considered a scientific theory. It is really an *ad hoc* device to explain away the existence of long-period comets, given the dogma of billions of years.

**Collisions would have destroyed most comets:** The classical Oort cloud is supposed to comprise comet nuclei left over from the evolutionary nebular-hypothesis origin of the solar system (see Chapter 1), with a total mass of about 40 Earths. But a newer study showed that collisions would have destroyed most of these, leaving a combined mass of comets equivalent to only about one Earth, or at most 3.5 Earths with some doubtful assumptions.[15,16]

**The 'fading problem':** The models predict about 100 times more NICs than are actually observed. So evolutionist astronomers postulate an 'arbitrary fading function'.[17] A recent proposal is that the

comets must disrupt before we get a chance to see them.[18] It seems desperate to propose an unobserved source to keep comets supplied for the alleged billions of years, then make excuses for why this hypothetical source doesn't feed in comets nearly as fast as it should.

### *Kuiper Belt*

The Kuiper Belt is supposed to be a doughnut-shaped reservoir of comets at about 30–50 AU (beyond Neptune's orbit), postulated as a source of short-period comets. It is named after Dutch astronomer Gerald Kuiper (1905–1973), sometimes considered the father of modern planetary science, who proposed it in 1951.

To remove the evolutionary dilemma, there must be *billions* of comet nuclei in the Kuiper Belt. But nowhere near this many objects have been found—only 1,248 as at December 2011.[19] Furthermore, the Kuiper Belt Objects (KBOs) discovered so far are much larger than comets. While the diameter of the nucleus of a typical comet is around 10 km, the recently discovered KBOs are over 100 km in diameter, so are at least ten times wider than comets, which means over a thousand times more massive. In fact, the KBOs Orcus and Quaoar are over 1,000 km in diameter.[20]

So in fact there has been no discovery of comets *per se* in the region of the hypothetical Kuiper Belt, so it so far is a non-answer.[21] Many astronomers, therefore, refer to the bodies as Trans-Neptunian Objects, which objectively describes their position beyond Neptune without any *assumptions* that they are related to a comet source as Kuiper wanted.

Furthermore, more recent observations indicate that the Kuiper Belt is too stable to be a comet reservoir. E.g. Quaoar has an almost circular orbit like the planets, not the hugely elongated comet-type orbit. So the source of short-period comets is now considered to be the 'Scattered Disc'.[22] This is even further out, and the bodies (Scattered Disc Objects, SDOs) have highly elliptical orbits from 30–35 AU at perihelion[23] to over 100 AU at aphelion[24]. However, much the same problems apply: too few objects, and too large. For example, the SDO Eris is about the same size as Pluto (see Chapter 14). Another SDO called Sedna is larger than Quaoar.

Credit: ESA

**Comet 67P/Churyumov–Gerasimenko as seen by space probe *Rosetta*. The unusual shape has generated much discussion about the reason for it. The largest lobe is 4.1 km (2.5 miles) long, and its orbital period is 6.44 years.**

## Oxygen in comet atmosphere supports biblical time frame.

In 2004, the European Space Agency launched the space probe *Rosetta* to study asteroids and comets. Ten years later, in November 2014, its lander *Philae* touched down on comet 67P/Churyumov–Gerasimenko—the first space mission to land on a comet.

Credit: ESA

**An artistic representation of the space probe *Rosetta* launching its lander *Philae* towards comet 67P/ Churyumov–Gerasimenko.**

Credit: ESA

**A photo illustration provided by the European Space Agency (ESA) of the *Philae* lander descending onto comet 67/ Churyumov–Gerasimenko**

The probe carried a mass spectrometer ROSINA (Rosetta Orbiter Spectrometer for Ion and Neutral Analysis). This made "the most surprising discovery" about the comet to date, according to Principal Investigator Kathrin Altwegg of the University of Bern, Switzerland.[25]

There was a lot of free oxygen gas ($O_2$) in the comet coma (atmosphere)—almost 4% as much as the most abundant gas, water vapour.[26] In fact, it was consistently high over seven months from September 2014 to March 2015.

However, this poses many problems for evolutionary models of the solar system,[27] and was most unexpected. The problem is that oxygen is very reactive, as Dr Altwegg explains: "We had never thought that oxygen could 'survive' for billions of years without combining with other substances."[25]

One possible source would be from ultraviolet (UV) light splitting water molecules into hydrogen and oxygen. But for most of the comet's lifetime, it would have been in the Kuiper Belt beyond Neptune. UV would be able to penetrate only a few metres to produce oxygen at that distance, but when the comet came into the inner solar system, all that material would have evaporated. This would remove any oxygen produced during its time in the Belt. So, is the oxygen being produced by UV in the comet's brief time nearer

**A time-lapse image of Halley's comet. This famous comet orbits retrograde to Earth, contrary to the nebular hypothesis.**

the sun? Apparently not, because we don't see large changes in oxygen concentration, nor do we find ozone ($O_3$), which is produced in our own atmosphere by UV attacking $O_2$ molecules.[28]

So the only remaining solution is that the oxygen was primordial: i.e. incorporated into the comet nucleus when it was formed. The researchers suggest that it came from UV radiation breaking off oxygen from water molecules in ice grains, the oxygen being trapped in voids in the ice, and those grains being incorporated into the comet. However, the researchers say, "Current Solar System formation models do not predict conditions that would allow this to occur."[26]

## Implication for chemical evolution

For the last six decades, it has been a widely believed myth that life on Earth evolved in a primordial soup.[29] The basic chemicals in the soup were allegedly generated by UV radiation and lightning in a primordial atmosphere unlike the present one. It was allegedly 'reducing', meaning it contained hydrogen-rich compounds like methane ($CH_4$) and ammonia ($NH_3$) and lacked oxygen. Our current 'oxidizing' atmosphere would prohibit all this, because oxygen would destroy the so-called building blocks, and indeed prevent their formation in the first place.

It surprises many to realize that this theory is not driven by evidence but by the dogma that life evolved by spontaneous generation—no intelligence allowed, by decree. But there is good evidence against this naturalistic hypothesis, from a highly oxidized form of the rare earth metal cerium ($Ce^{4+}$) found in zircons 'dated' at 4.35 billion years old.[30,31] Now this enigmatic discovery of primordial oxygen in a comet is further evidence that we can't rule out primordial oxygen on Earth either.

## Summary

Comets are not portents of doom, but are objects God created on Day 4 of Creation Week. The successful prediction of comet appearances was an early triumph for modern science, inspired by a biblical worldview. Comets lose so much mass every time they shine that they could not be billions of years old. Evolutionists propose various sources to replenish the comet supply, but there is no real observational evidence, and numerous unsolved theoretical difficulties. Therefore comets make much more sense within a biblical timescale.

Comets only thousands of years old are no accident. As the Psalmist (19:1) wrote, "The heavens declare the glory of God, the skies proclaim the work of his hands."

## References and Notes

1. This chapter adapted and updated from Sarfati, J., *Creation* **25**(3):36–40, 2003; creation.com/comets-portents-of-doom-or-indicators-of-youth

2. For example in Newton, I., *The Chronology of Ancient Kingdoms Amended*, published posthumously 1728, cited in Renfrew, C., *Before Civilization*, Penguin Books, England, pp. 22–23, 1973.

3. Some have thought that this was the 'Star of Bethlehem', but it doesn't fit the details given in Matthew's Gospel. Rather, this Star is better explained as an appearance of God's Shekinah Glory—creation.com/starbeth.

4. See Q&A: Young Age Evidence, CMI website creation.com/young.

5. Frank Whipple's model, e.g., Whipple, F.L., Background of modern comet theory, *Nature* **263**(5572):15–19, 2 September 1976. He expressed it more formally as "dirty ice comet nucleus".

6. Whipple, F.L., Present status of the icy conglomerate model; in: *Ices in the Solar System*, Klinger J., Benest, D., Dollfus, A. and Smoluchowski, R. (Eds.), D. Reidel Publishing, Dordrecht, Holland, pp. 343–366, 1984.

7. Comet Grigg–Skjellerup was discovered by John Grigg of New Zealand in 1902 and rediscovered on its next appearance by John Skjellerup (an Australian in South Africa) in 1922. John Grigg's grandson, Russell Grigg, is the Editor of this book.

8. However, the pathetic appearance at its last visit in 1986 was more due to the highly unfortunate conditions. I.e. when it was at its brightest, at perihelion (closest approach to the sun), the Earth was on the other side of the sun, which therefore blocked it. And even when it emerged from behind the sun, it was far from Earth.

9. Sarfati, J., Will Comet Elenin destroy us? *Creation* **34**(1): 51–53, 2012; creation.com/elenin.

10. Wieland, C., Halley's Comet: beacon of creation, *Creation* **8**(2):6–10, 1986; creation.com/halley.

11. The most thorough article is Faulkner, D., Comets and the age of the solar system, *J. Creation* **11**(3):264–273, 1997; creation.com/comet.

12. AU = Astronomical Unit, the mean distance from the centre of the earth to the centre of the sun, ~150 million km (~93 million miles).

13. This comes from Kepler's 3rd Law of Planetary motion, $a^3 = kp^2$, where $a$ is the semi-major axis in AU, $p$ is the period in years, and $k$ is a proportionality constant.

14. Sagan, C. and Druyan, A., *Comet*, Michael Joseph, London, p. 175, 1985.

15. Stern, S.A. and Weissman, P.R., Rapid collisional evolution of comets during the formation of the Oort cloud, *Nature* **409**(6820):589–591, 2001.

16. Faulkner, D., More problems for the 'Oort comet cloud', *J. Creation* **15**(2):11, 2001; creation.com/oort.

17. Bailey, M.E., Where have all the comets gone? *Science* **296**(5576):2251–2253, 21 June 2002 (perspective on Levison, ref. 18).

18. Levison, H.F. *et al.*, The mass disruption of Oort Cloud comets, *Science* **296**(5576):2212–2215, 21 June 2002.

19. Parker, J.M. (Ed.), *Distant EKOs: The Kuiper Belt Electronic Newsletter* **78**, December 2011; boulder.swri.edu/ekonews/issues/past/n078/html/index.html.

20. The name 'Quaoar' (pronounced kwah-o-wahr) comes from the creation mythology of the Tongva people (the San Gabrielino native Americans). It was discovered by Chad Trujillo and Mike Brown of Caltech in Pasadena in June 2002.

21. Newton, R., The short-period comets 'problem' (for evolutionists): Have recent 'Kuiper Belt' discoveries solved the evolutionary/long-age dilemma? *J. Creation* **16**(2)15–17, 2002; creation.com/kuiper.

22. Levison H.F. and Donnes, L., Comet Populations and Cometary Dynamics in McFadden, L.A.A. *et al.*, *Encyclopedia of the Solar System* (2nd ed.), Amsterdam; Boston: Academic Press, pp. 575–588, 2007.

23. Closest point to the sun, from Greek περὶ *perí* around; and ἥλιος *hēlios*, sun.

24. Furthest point from the sun, from Greek ἀπό *apó*, from, which becomes ἀπ-*ap*- or ἀφ- *aph*- before an unaspirated or aspirated vowel, respectively.

25. Sample, S., Rosetta finds oxygen on comet 67P in 'most surprising discovery to date': Oxygen revealed to be fourth most abundant gas in the comet's atmosphere, contradicting long-held theories of comet formation, *Guardian* (UK), 29 October 2015.

26. Bieler, A. *et al.*, Abundant molecular oxygen in the coma of comet 67P/Churyumov-Gerasimenko, *Nature* **526**(7575):678-81, 29 October 2015 | doi:10.1038/nature15707.

27. Cesare, C., Rosetta sniffs oxygen around comet 67P: The presence of the gas could have implications for theories of the early Solar System, *Nature News*, 28 October 2015.

28. UV breaks $O_2$ into reactive oxygen atoms, O, which then attack other $O_2$ molecules: $O_2 \rightarrow 2O$; then $O + O_2 \rightarrow O_3$.

29. For critiques, see *Evolution's Achilles' Heels*, ch. 3, CBP, 2014; available from creation.com/s/10-2-640; Batten, D., Origin of life: An explanation of what is needed for abiogenesis (or biopoiesis), creation.com/origin-of-life, 26 November 2013.

30. Trail, D. *et al.*, The oxidation state of Hadean magmas and implications for early Earth's atmosphere, *Nature* 480:79-82, 01 December 2011 | doi:10.1038/nature10655.

31. Sarfati, J., The Miller-Urey experiment revisited, creation.com/miller3, 15 March 2015.

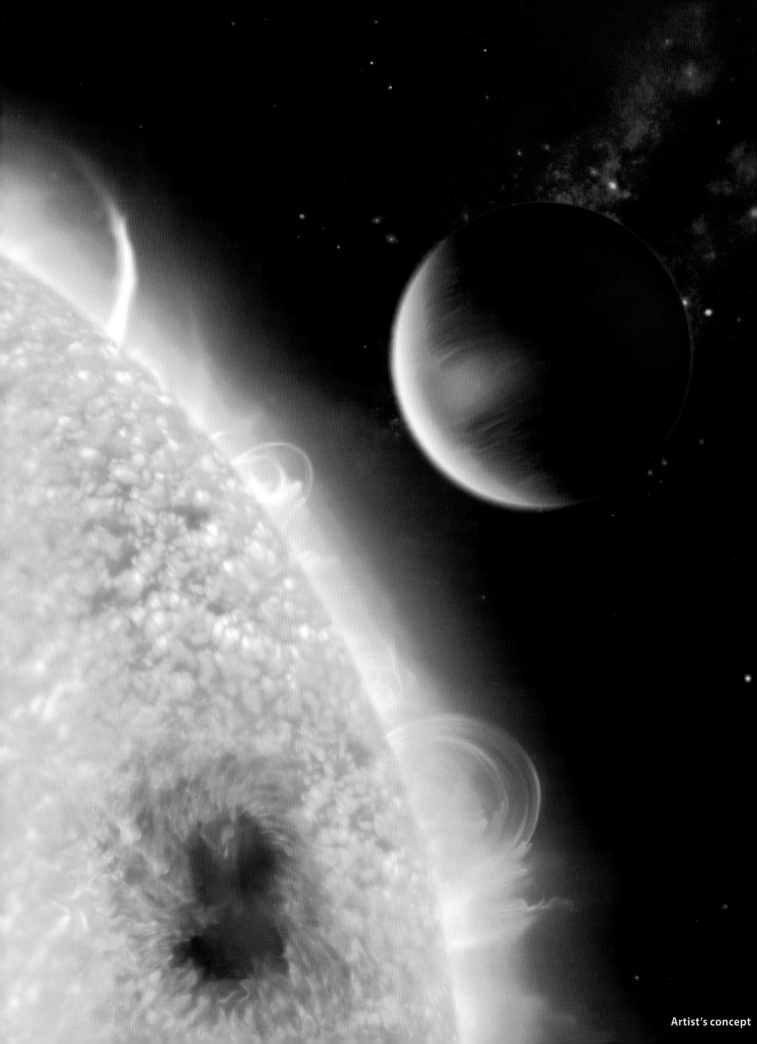

Artist's concept

# Chapter 16

# Exoplanets: Planets around other stars

Many evolutionists have long hoped to find evidence of life in space. They reason that if life evolved on Earth, then it could have evolved elsewhere. If, as the argument goes, there are countless planets throughout the universe that have formed via natural processes, then there must be other Earth-like planets. Many think that finding such a planet outside our solar system would be almost like finding evidence of life in space. Scientists have searched for years for planets orbiting other stars. These are called extrasolar planets, or exoplanets.

**Author: Wayne Spencer[1]**

The first evidence of extrasolar planets around a sun-like star was in 1995 with the discovery of a planet orbiting star 51-Pegasi.[2] Prior to this there were various reports of possible exoplanets but some of them turned out to be brown dwarf stars, and some were controversial cases involving planets orbiting pulsars.

These 'pulsar planets' were controversial due to questions about the observational evidence.[3] Pulsar PSR 1257+12 was reported to have two exoplanets in 1992 but it was controversial for a few years. Scientists now consider at least the original two exoplanets reported around this pulsar to be confirmed. Today research teams around the world are searching for extrasolar planets with greatly refined techniques. As of July 2016, some 3,371 objects have been catalogued as confirmed exoplanets; 'confirmed' means they have been verified by multiple research teams.[4]

An artist's concept of the hot Jupiter exoplanet 51 Pegasi b, first nicknamed 'Bellerophon', then 'Dimidium'. This was the first exoplanet around a normal star; it was found in 1995. Half the mass of Jupiter, it orbits very close to its sun every 4 (Earth) days, so its year is 4 days long, and its estimated temperature is 1,200° C

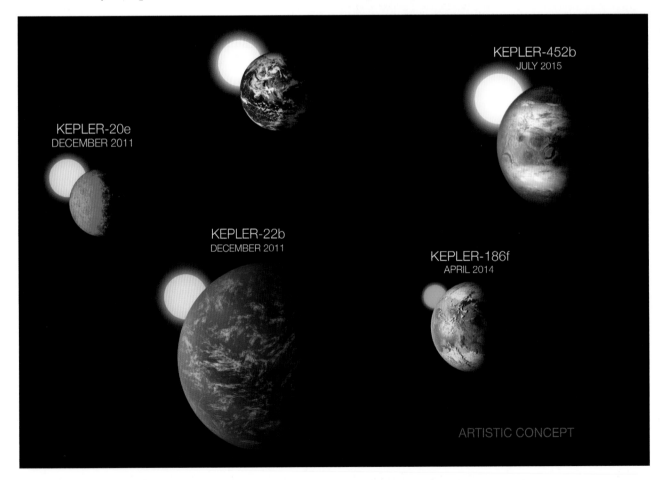

An artist's concept of some of the planets discovered by (and so named after) the *Kepler* space telescope. Kepler 20e is smaller than Earth but scorching hot. Kepler 22b is more than twice Earth size and is unlikely to have a solid surface. Kepler 186f orbits a cool M dwarf star. Kepler 452b is a near-Earth-size planet orbiting a star similar to our sun.

An artist's impression of *Kepler*, NASA's space telescope for the purpose of discovering planets orbiting other stars. Named after the Renaissance astronomer Johannes Kepler, it was launched on March 7, 2009, into an Earth-trailing, heliocentric orbit.

One of these is the exoplanet HD 189733b (see the artist's concept of it orbiting its star at the beginning of this chapter). It is about the size of Jupiter, but is over 30 times closer to its star than Earth is to our sun, so it is termed a 'hot Jupiter'. Obviously it could not support life.

## Biblical perspective

Creationists need to answer two main questions regarding exoplanets. 1) Do they exist? and 2) How did they form? The first question has to do with empirical evidence, but the second has to do with origins science. Scripture does not tell us whether other stars have planets, so we must apply the best observational science we can to answer the question.

On the other hand, Scripture is clear that God supernaturally created the earth and the rest of the universe within six consecutive, normal-length days and that the universe is relatively young.[5] Thus, if the observational evidence for exoplanets is sound, which I believe it is (see below), creationists will differ with secular scientists about how and when they formed, not whether they exist.

## The origin of exoplanets

As scientists came to the conclusion that extrasolar planets exist, they faced challenges in explaining their origin. From a creation point of view, it is most likely that God created exoplanets on Day 4 of Creation Week, along with the luminaries (stars), and He could have created them with any characteristics He wished. Our own solar system is special because of Earth—our system and our planet are designed to be a safe and stable environment for life. Isaiah 45:18 acknowledges this: "He did not create it [Earth] to be empty; he formed it to be inhabited."

Not only is Earth special in being designed for life, but our sun is also designed to allow for life. In extrasolar planetary systems, it is not only the temperature of a planet that may be a problem for it supporting life, the star the exoplanet orbits can also make life unlikely. But in our solar system the earth and sun are a designed system for our provision.

However, there are significant scientific problems with attempts to explain the formation of stars and planets from clouds of gas and dust.[6,7] One main issue is that the hypothetical disk of gas and dust tends to dissipate too fast for the resulting planets to become as large as they are observed to be. There are other major problems:

## Migrating planets

Many extrasolar planets orbit extremely close to their stars—even closer than Mercury is to the sun. Thus they are far too hot for many materials to condense and pull together by gravity. A few exoplanets even lose matter to the star, or from their gases being essentially 'boiled away'.

To address this problem, evolutionary astronomers proposed that planets could form far away from the star and then the orbit could move inward. This is referred to as *orbit migration*. This would allow the planets to form in a cooler region of their stellar system, but then the orbit would shrink, due to friction from the dust disk slowing the planet, to put the planet where we see it now.

The idea can also be applied in other ways. For example, in our own solar system, astronomers realize that there would have been too little material at the distance of Uranus and Neptune to form these giants, so they proposed that they formed *closer* to our sun, then migrated *outward* to their current orbits.[8]

Orbit migration theories have difficulties because the dust disk around the star tends to dissipate before the planet can grow large enough or before it can come to its observed position.[9]

## Reversed and slanted orbits

Now a new problem for planet origin theories has surfaced. A technique has been developed to determine a planet's orbital tilt relative to the equator of the star. Several exoplanets actually have *retrograde orbits*[10]— in the opposite direction of the star's spin. Other exoplanets have very large orbital inclinations (slants), some more than 80°.

These strange orbits create a serious problem for planet formation models because a planet is said to get the momentum for its orbit from the dust disk from which it formed. Thus planetary orbits should initially be in the same plane as the equator of the star, and in the same direction as the star's rotation. But there is no plausible way that a dust disk can give rise to a planet with an orbital tilt of 80°, let alone a retrograde orbit.

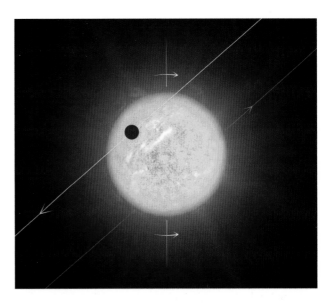

**An artist's concept of an exoplanet in retrograde orbit around its star, i.e. in the opposite direction to the rotation of the star. Many exoplanets orbit this way. This is a contradiction to evolutionary theories of planet formation.**

Evolutionary planetary scientists are generally trying to answer this by assuming that where the planet orbit is highly inclined or retrograde, there was once one or more other planets (or possibly stars) in the stellar system that were also at highly inclined orbits. If there are multiple objects (stars or planets) in various highly inclined orbits, then this could possibly cause some complex orbit changes.[11]

Some scientists believe that where there are three or more stars and planets in a system, it is possible for a planet's orbit to become highly inclined. But this must assume that objects once existed in these systems at large distances from their star, which we cannot or do not observe (and where did they come from?). It is also questionable that this highly unlikely process could happen for all the known cases of retrograde planets.

## Implications

Certainly extrasolar planetary systems differ from our solar system. They show that God created variety in the universe and that our own planet was created with design and purpose. Astronomers are gaining the ability to detect Earth-sized exoplanets. But we must not confuse an Earth-*sized* planet as being a truly Earth-*like* planet. It is no accident that Earth is in the so-called 'habitable zone' in our solar system—a narrow range of distances from the sun where liquid water can exist.

**NASA admits our "eight-planet solar system is unique"!**

No extrasolar planets are known to be habitable—lifeless Venus and Mars are more 'Earth-like'. In fact, even if a planet very much like Earth were eventually discovered, with an appropriate atmosphere and liquid water, that does not in and of itself mean that life could evolve on such a planet. We depend on our Creator for the planet we have and that He created and sustains life.

# The evidence for extrasolar planets
## (technical details)

Although there were initially unrealistic claims about exoplanets due to bias and wishful thinking,[12] there is now sound observational evidence for the existence of planets orbiting other stars. Even today scientists still occasionally make mistakes in exoplanet research. The evidence for the existence of exoplanets has come from two primary methods, and other recently developed methods, in order of the percentage of planets detected:[13]

## 1. Transit or photometric method

This measures the slight drop in a star's brightness as a planet passes in front of it. This won't work for most stars, because the planet must block Earth's line of sight. Transit measurements have revealed exoplanets orbiting well over 100 stars. Many more are being reported at a rapid pace. The silhouette of a planet transiting a star gives the planet's size and the star's

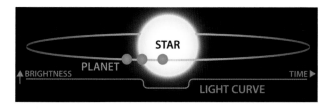

light skirting the planet can indicate the composition of any atmosphere.

Many of the exoplanets studied this way seem to be large gaseous planets like Jupiter or Saturn in our own solar system. Combining a planet's diameter with the estimate of its mass gives its density. There is at least one known case of an exoplanet that has a similar density to Earth.[14] A significant portion of this planet's mass must be rock.

If the transit dimming of a star is in time with wobbling, this is especially strong evidence for a planet.

## 2. Doppler or radial velocity method

Astronomers measure very precisely the spectrum of the star's light. An extrasolar planet can cause a periodic change in the motion of the star as it orbits, essentially making the star wobble and causing tiny variations in the colour of the light,[15] due to the Doppler effect.[16] If a planet is more massive or it is close to the star, then it causes a larger 'wobble' on the star than if it were smaller or farther away. Planets that are farther away from their stars cause slower wobbles because the planets orbit more slowly.[17]

Astronomers have used this technique to discover many exoplanets and sometimes multiple planets. But while the Doppler method can estimate a planet's mass and distance from its star, it can't tell us the planet's composition.

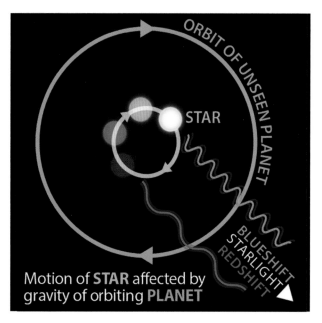

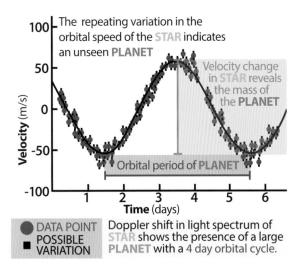

100 — The repeating variation in the orbital speed of the STAR indicates an unseen PLANET

Velocity change in STAR reveals the mass of the PLANET

Orbital period of PLANET

Velocity (m/s)

Time (days)

● DATA POINT
■ POSSIBLE VARIATION

Doppler shift in light spectrum of STAR shows the presence of a large PLANET with a 4 day orbital cycle.

## 3. Direct imaging

In 2009, NASA launched the Kepler Mission, a space observatory placed in Earth's orbit, designed for very precise transit measurements of extrasolar planets. One such claimed photographed exoplanet orbits a nearby star called Fomalhaut. Called Fomalhaut b or Dagon, it orbits just inside a dust ring.[18] Fomalhaut b has been debated by scientists. It seems to be surrounded by dust from a large dust ring that exists around the star, but it can be seen by powerful telescopes in infrared light. The *Hubble Space Telescope* took photos of Fomalhaut b over two years, showing that this object was in motion around the star. The *Spitzer Space Telescope* has also detected infrared radiation from two hot Jupiter-like exoplanets.[19]

Direct imaging techniques are discovering more exoplanets, as astronomers use ever improving technology. Direct imaging verifies observations from the other methods and is especially applicable for cases where the planet is located at greater distances from the star. Direct imaging also provides some information about the composition of the exoplanet.

## 4. Gravitational microlensing

According to Einstein's General Theory of Relativity, very strong gravity can bend light, and that has been demonstrated numerous times. So a star can act as a lens that magnifies light of another star, if both are almost exactly in the same line of sight from the earth. The gravity of a planet can add to the lensing.

This technique can pick up planets that the first two techniques will miss: planets in wide orbits that

are perpendicular to the line of site. However, the detection is unrepeatable because the stars will move out of alignment, and the method usually can't provide much more information than the planet's mass.

# Kepler 78b: The scorching lava world that shouldn't exist
## By David Catchpoole

Scientists today repeatedly encounter evidence that thwarts theories of evolutionary origins and long-age timelines.[20] An example is the exoplanet Kepler-78b, about 20% larger than Earth and weighing twice as much, recently discovered[21] in the constellation Cygnus. Its discovery is so confronting to planetary formation theories that a media release by the Harvard Smithsonian Center for Astrophysics (CfA) proclaimed, "Kepler-78b is a planet that shouldn't exist."[22]

The evolutionary astronomers are primarily fretting about the closeness[23] of "this scorching lava world"[24] to its star, circling it in only eight and a half hours—one of the tightest known orbits in the universe. In fact, it is 40 times closer to its star than Mercury is to our sun. This makes it 'an abomination'[25] to current planet formation theories, because Kepler-78b's present orbit would have been *inside* its own star early in the mooted evolutionary origins of this planetary system, when the star is said to have been much larger. That is of course impossible, as CfA astronomer Dimitar Sasselov explained:

"It couldn't have formed in place because you can't form a planet inside a star. It couldn't have formed further out and migrated inward, because it would have migrated all the way into the star. This planet is an enigma."[265]

Fellow CfA astronomer David Latham echoed, "This planet is a complete mystery. We don't know how it formed or how it got to where it is today."[5]

Kepler-78b is only one such 'complete mystery' of *many* 'exoplanet enigmas' discovered of late.[6] It underlines once again the failure of all attempts to explain the formation of planets naturalistically.[7] Surely there's a message there, for anyone willing to receive: "The heavens declare the glory of God, and the sky above proclaims his handiwork." (Psalm 19:1)

Exoplanet Kepler 78b is just slightly larger than Earth, but it orbits a star 40 times closer to it than Mercury is to our sun. At such a scorching distance, even rock is liquid. The fact that an exoplanet is about the size of Earth is no indication that it might support life.

## References and Notes

1. This chapter adapted and updated from Spencer, W., *Creation* **33**(1):45–47, 2011; creation.com/extrasolar-planets-problems-for-evolution.
2. Mayor, M.; Queloz, D., A Jupiter-mass companion to a solar-type star, *Nature* **378**(6555):355–359, 1995.
3. Pulsar PSR 1257+12 was reported to have two exoplanets in 1992 but it was controversial for a few years. Scientists now consider at least the original two exoplanets reported around this pulsar to be confirmed. This pulsar may have one or two other exoplanets as well.
4. NASA *PlanetQuest* website, planetquest.jpl.nasa.gov, accessed 29 July 2016.
5. Batten, D., Catchpoole, D., Sarfati, J. and Wieland, C., *The Creation Answers Book*, ch. 2, Creation Book Publishers, 2008.
6. Spencer, W., The origin and history of the solar system, *in:* Walsh, R.E. (Ed.), *Proceedings of the Third International Conference on Creationism*, pp. 513–523, Creation Science Fellowship Inc., Pittsburgh, PA, 1994.
7. Henry, J., Solar system formation by accretion has no observational evidence, *J. Creation* **24**(2): 87–94, 2010; creation.com/accretion-hypothesis. For a lay article, see Chapter 1 Solar system origin: Nebular hypothesis.
8. This involves a complex theory where the dust disk as well as the other existing planets change the positions of Uranus and Neptune. See Spencer, W., Migrating planets and migrating theories, *J. Creation* **21**(3):12–14, 2007, as well as this book, Chapters 12 and 13.
9. For example, for one exoplanet, WASP-18b, estimates suggest the planet should have fallen into the star in about 650,000 years after formation, much less than the presumed evolutionary age of billions of years. Another problem is, how could the dust disk last long enough to move the planet several Astronomical Units from the cold region where it formed to close to the star where it is observed today? See Spencer, W., The search for Earth-like planets, *J. Creation* **24**(1):72–76, 2010; creation.com/earthsearch.
10. Turning planetary theory upside down, *Royal Astronomical Society*, 13 April 2010; www.eso.org/public/news/eso/1016.
11. Fabrycky, D. and Tremaine, S., Shrinking binary and planetary orbits by Kozai Cycles with tidal friction, *Astrophysical Journal* **669**(2):669–1298, 2007.
12. Kalas, P., Dusty disks and planet mania, *Science* **281**(5374): 182–183, 10 July 1998; Planet mania, *Creation* **21**(1):7, 1998; creation.com/focus-211#planet.
13. exoplanets.jpl.nasa.gov.
14. COROT discovers smallest exoplanet yet, with a surface to walk on, *European Space Agency News*, 3 February 2009, www.esa.int. But no one is *really* likely to walk on it, since its temperature is between 1000 and 1500° C!
15. When the star is moving towards us, the light is 'blue-shifted', i.e. to a shorter wavelength, and when it's moving away, we see a 'red shift'.
16. This may seem difficult to believe, but our own sun actually wobbles as it moves through space as well, due to the gravitational pull of Jupiter and the other planets. Boss, Alan, *Looking for Earths: The Race to Find New Solar Systems*, pp. 8–9, John Wiley & Sons, Inc., New York, 1998.
17. The creationist astronomer Johannes Kepler (1571–1630) discovered that the square of the planet's period is proportional to the cube of its distance from the sun, *Creation* **15**(1):40–43, 1992; creation.com/kepler. See also Appendix.
18. Kalas, P. *et al.*, Optical images of an exosolar planet 25 light-years from Earth, *Science* **322**(5906):1345–1348, 2008. Fomalhaut, in the constellation Piscis Australis ('Southern Fish'), is only 25 light years from earth, so is one of the brightest stars in the southern sky.
19. Naeye, R., Exoplanets: The heat is on, skyandtelescope.com/news, 23 March 2005. 'Hot Jupiters' are giant planets orbiting very close to their star. They also noted that the infrared radiation dimmed when the planet disappeared behind the star.
20. Batten, D., Age of the earth—101 evidences for a young age of the earth and the universe, creation.com/age, 4 June 2009.
21. By means of data sent from the telescope on NASA's Kepler spacecraft launched in 2009, and later confirmed using measurements from the high-precision spectrometer HARPS-North at the Roque de los Muchachos Observatory on La Palma and the HIRES spectrograph at the Keck Observatory, Hawaii.
22. Mystery world baffles astronomers, Harvard Smithsonian Center for Astrophysics media release no. 2013-25, cfa.harvard.edu, 30 October 2013.
23. Less than 1.6 million km (1 million miles).
24. O'Neill, I., Kepler-78b: Mystery exoplanet shouldn't even exist, news.discovery.com, 30 October 2013.
25. Planets baffle big bangers, *Creation* **36**(3):9, 2014; creation.com/focus-363#planets.
26. Hartnett, J.G., Planetary system formation: exposing naturalistic storytelling; creation.com/planet-formation, 14 April 2016. Also, Psarris, S., *Our created solar system* DVD (available from CMI, creation.com/s/30-9-587).

# Appendix

## The colourizing of space images

Most of the planet images in this book have been colourized. This is because the space cameras do not use colour film (or any film at all), but record the images with special electronic detectors in shades of black and white. Finished colour images are combinations of black-and-white exposures to which

colour has been added during processing to enhance an object's detail.

For example, NASA advises that the image of Mars (Chapter 9) was constructed from three different black-and-white images recording red, green, and blue light reflected from the planet, as in the illustration.

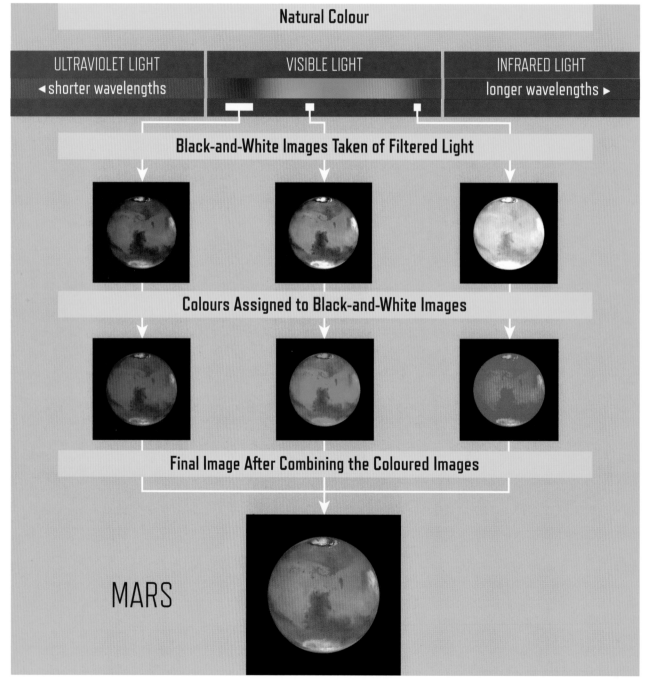

Credit: NASA/Hubble's Color Toolbox

## Kepler's laws of planetary motion

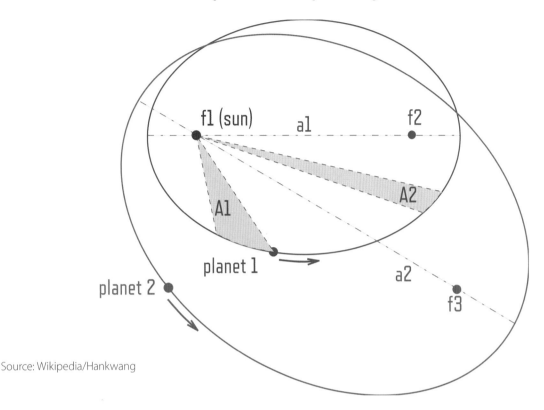

Source: Wikipedia/Hankwang

The motion of the planets in our sun-centred solar system is governed by three laws of planetary motion originally formulated by the creationist astronomer Johannes Kepler (1571–1630) in the 1600s.

1. The orbit of a planet is an ellipse with the sun at one of the two foci.
2. A line segment joining a planet and the sun sweeps out equal areas during equal intervals of time.
3. The square of the orbital period of a planet is proportional to the cube of the semi-major axis of its orbit.

In the diagram, the elliptical orbits of two planets are shown in red and green. The focal points for planet 1 are f1 and f2, and those for planet 2 are f1 and f3.

The sun is at focal point f1.

The two shaded areas A1 and A2 have the same area. The time taken for planet 1 to traverse the orbital border of these two areas is the same. A comet travels faster as it approaches the sun, and slower as it moves away from the sun.

The total orbit times for planet 1 and planet 2 have a ratio of $a_1^{3/2} : a_2^{3/2}$.

## Commonly used terms

**Astronomical Unit** (AU) is the mean distance from the centre of the earth to the centre of the sun, now defined by the International Astronomical Union as exactly 149,597,870,700 metres (i.e. about 150 million kilometres, or 93 million miles).

**Light year** (ly) is the *distance* light travels in a vacuum in one Julian year of 365.25 days, namely 9,460, 730,472,580.8 km (or nearly 6 million million miles).

**Evolutionary dates**: Ga = giga-annum or a billion ($10^9$) years ago; Ma = mega-annum or a million years ago; ka = kilo-annum or a thousand years ago.

**Evolutionary duration**, Gyr = a billion years; Myr = a million years; kyr = a thousand years; e.g. evolutionists believe that the Mesozoic Era was 252–65 Ma, thus it supposedly lasted 187 Myr.

# Solar System Fact Sheet (Data from NASA)

| | MERCURY | VENUS | EARTH | MOON | MARS | JUPITER | SATURN | URANUS | NEPTUNE | PLUTO |
|---|---|---|---|---|---|---|---|---|---|---|
| **Mass (1024kg)** | 0.330 | 4.87 | 5.97 | 0.073 | 0.642 | 1898 | 568 | 86.8 | 102 | 0.0146 |
| **Diameter (km)** | 4879 | 12,104 | 12,756 | 3475 | 6792 | 142,984 | 120,536 | 51,118 | 49,528 | 2370 |
| **Density (kg/m3)** | 5427 | 5243 | 5514 | 3340 | 3933 | 1326 | 687 | 1271 | 1638 | 2095 |
| **Gravity (m/s2)** | 3.7 | 8.9 | 9.8 | 1.6 | 3.7 | 23.1 | 9.0 | 8.7 | 11.0 | 0.7 |
| **Escape Velocity (km/s)** | 4.3 | 10.4 | 11.2 | 2.4 | 5.0 | 59.5 | 35.5 | 21.3 | 23.5 | 1.3 |
| **Rotation Period (hours)** | 1407.6 | -5832.5 | 23.9 | 655.7 | 24.6 | 9.9 | 10.7 | -17.2 | 16.1 | -153.3 |
| **Length of Day (hours)** | 4222.6 | 2802.0 | 24.0 | 708.7 | 24.7 | 9.9 | 10.7 | 17.2 | 16.1 | 153.3 |
| **Distance from Sun (106 km)** | 57.9 | 108.2 | 149.6 | 0.384* | 227.9 | 778.6 | 1433.5 | 2872.5 | 4495.1 | 5906.4 |
| **Perihelion (106 km)** | 46.0 | 107.5 | 147.1 | 0.363* | 206.6 | 740.5 | 1352.6 | 2741.3 | 4444.5 | 4436.8 |
| **Aphelion (106 km)** | 69.8 | 108.9 | 152.1 | 0.406* | 249.2 | 816.6 | 1514.5 | 3003.6 | 4545.7 | 7375.9 |
| **Orbital Period (days)** | 88.0 | 224.7 | 365.2 | 27.3 | 687.0 | 4331 | 10,747 | 30,589 | 59,800 | 90,560 |
| **Orbital Velocity (km/s)** | 47.4 | 35.0 | 29.8 | 1.0 | 24.1 | 13.1 | 9.7 | 6.8 | 5.4 | 4.7 |
| **Orbital Inclination (degrees)** | 7.0 | 3.4 | 0.0 | 5.1 | 1.9 | 1.3 | 2.5 | 0.8 | 1.8 | 17.2 |
| **Orbital Eccentricity** | 0.205 | 0.007 | 0.017 | 0.055 | 0.094 | 0.049 | 0.057 | 0.046 | 0.011 | 0.244 |
| **Obliquity to Orbit (degrees)** | 0.01 | 177.4 | 23.4 | 6.7 | 25.2 | 3.1 | 26.7 | 97.8 | 28.3 | 122.5 |
| **Mean Temperature (C)** | 167 | 464 | 15 | -20 | -65 | -110 | -140 | -195 | -200 | -225 |
| **Surface Pressure (bars)** | 0 | 92 | 1 | 0 | 0.01 | Unknown* | Unknown* | Unknown* | Unknown* | 0 |
| **Number of Moons** | 0 | 0 | 1 | 0 | 2 | 67 | 62 | 27 | 14 | 5 |
| **Ring System?** | No | No | No | No | No | Yes | Yes | Yes | Yes | No |
| **Global Magnetic Field?** | Yes | No | Yes | No | No | Yes | Yes | Yes | Yes | Unknown |
| | MERCURY | VENUS | EARTH | MOON | MARS | JUPITER | SATURN | URANUS | NEPTUNE | PLUTO |

* See Fact Sheet Notes (NASA)

## Solar System Fact Sheet—Ratio to Earth Values (Data from NASA)

| | MERCURY | VENUS | EARTH | MOON | MARS | JUPITER | SATURN | URANUS | NEPTUNE | PLUTO |
|---|---|---|---|---|---|---|---|---|---|---|
| **Mass** | 0.0553 | 0.815 | 1 | 0.0123 | 0.107 | 317.8 | 95.2 | 14.5 | 17.1 | 0.0025 |
| **Diameter** | 0.383 | 0.949 | 1 | 0.2724 | 0.532 | 11.21 | 9.45 | 4.01 | 3.88 | 0.186 |
| **Density** | 0.984 | 0.951 | 1 | 0.605 | 0.713 | 0.240 | 0.125 | 0.230 | 0.297 | 0.380 |
| **Gravity** | 0.378 | 0.907 | 1 | 0.166 | 0.377 | 2.36 | 0.916 | 0.889 | 1.12 | 0.071 |
| **Escape Velocity** | 0.384 | 0.926 | 1 | 0.213 | 0.450 | 5.32 | 3.17 | 1.90 | 2.10 | 0.116 |
| **Rotation Period** | 58.8 | -244 | 1 | 27.4 | 1.03 | 0.415 | 0.445 | -0.720 | 0.673 | 6.41 |
| **Length of Day** | 175.9 | 116.8 | 1 | 29.5 | 1.03 | 0.414 | 0.444 | 0.718 | 0.671 | 6.39 |
| **Distance from Sun** | 0.387 | 0.723 | 1 | 0.00257* | 1.52 | 5.20 | 9.58 | 19.20 | 30.05 | 39.48 |
| **Perihelion** | 0.313 | 0.731 | 1 | 0.00247* | 1.41 | 5.03 | 9.20 | 18.64 | 30.22 | 30.16 |
| **Aphelion** | 0.459 | 0.716 | 1 | 0.00267* | 1.64 | 5.37 | 9.96 | 19.75 | 29.89 | 48.49 |
| **Orbital Period** | 0.241 | 0.615 | 1 | 0.0748 | 1.88 | 11.9 | 29.4 | 83.7 | 163.7 | 247.9 |
| **Orbital Velocity** | 1.59 | 1.18 | 1 | 0.0343 | 0.808 | 0.439 | 0.325 | 0.228 | 0.182 | 0.157 |
| **Orbital Eccentricity** | 12.3 | 0.401 | 1 | 3.29 | 5.60 | 2.93 | 3.38 | 2.74 | 0.677 | 14.6 |
| **Obliquity to Orbit** | 0.0004 | 0.113* | 1 | 0.285 | 1.07 | 0.134 | 1.14 | 4.17* | 1.21 | 2.45* |
| **Surface Pressure** | 0 | 92 | 1 | 0 | 0.01 | Unknown* | Unknown* | Unknown* | Unknown* | 0 |
| | MERCURY | VENUS | EARTH | MOON | MARS | JUPITER | SATURN | URANUS | NEPTUNE | PLUTO |

* See Fact Sheet Notes

## Fact Sheet Notes (NASA)

(Explanations of the headings and vaules in the Fact Sheet)

**Mass** ($10^{24}$kg). This is the mass of the planet in septillion (1 followed by 24 zeros) kilograms.

**Diameter** (km). The diameter of the planet at the equator, the distance through the centre of the planet from one point on the equator to the opposite side, in kilometres.

**Density** (kg/m$^3$). The average density (mass divided by volume) of the whole planet (not including the atmosphere for the terrestrial planets) in kilograms per cubic metre.

**Gravity** (m/s$^2$). The gravitational acceleration on the surface at the equator in metres per second squared, including the effects of rotation. For the gas giant planets the gravity is given at the 1 bar pressure level in the atmosphere. The gravity on Earth is designated as 1 'G', so the Ratio to Earth fact sheet gives the gravity of the other planets in Gs.

**Escape Velocity** (km/s). Initial velocity, in kilometres per second needed at the surface (at the 1 bar pressure level for the gas giants) to escape the body's gravitational pull, ignoring atmospheric drag.

**Rotation Period** (hours). This is the time it takes for the planet to complete one rotation relative to the fixed background stars (not relative to the sun) in hours. Negative numbers indicate retrograde (backwards relative to the Earth) rotation.

**Length of Day** (hours). The average time in hours for the sun to move from the noon position in the sky at a point on the equator back to the same position.

**Distance from Sun** ($10^6$ km). This is the average distance from the planet to the sun in millions of kilometres, also known as the semi-major axis. All planets have orbits which are elliptical, not perfectly circular, so there is a point in the orbit at which the planet is closest to the sun, the perihelion, and a point furthest from the sun, the aphelion. The average distance from the sun is midway between these two values. The average distance from the earth to the sun is defined as 1 Astronomical Unit (AU), so the Ratio table gives this distance in AU.

For the moon, the average distance from the earth is given.

**Perihelion, Aphelion** ($10^6$ km). The closest and furthest points in a planet's orbit about the sun, see "Distance from Sun" above.

For the moon, the closest and furthest points to Earth are given, known as the 'perigee' and 'apogee' respectively.

**Orbital Period** (days). This is the time in Earth days for a planet to orbit the sun from one vernal equinox to the next. Also known as the tropical orbit period, this is equal to a year on Earth.

For the moon, the sidereal orbit period, the time to orbit once relative to the fixed background stars, is given. The time from full moon to full moon, or sidereal period, is 29.53 days. For Pluto, the tropical orbital period is not well known, the sidereal orbital period is used.

**Orbital Velocity** (km/s). The average velocity or speed of the planet as it orbits the sun, in kilometres per second.

**Orbital Inclination**. The angle in degrees at which a planet orbits the sun is tilted relative to the ecliptic plane. The ecliptic plane is defined as the plane containing the earth's orbit, so the earth's inclination is 0.

**Orbital Eccentricity**. This is a measure of how far a planet's orbit about the sun (or the moon's orbit about the earth) is from being circular. The larger the eccentricity, the more elongated is the orbit, an eccentricity of 0 means the orbit is a perfect circle. There are no units for eccentricity.

**Obliquity to Orbit**. The angle in degrees the axis of a planet (the imaginary line running through the centre of the planet from the north to south poles) is tilted relative to a line perpendicular to the planet's orbit around the sun, postive pole defined by right hand rule.

Venus rotates in a retrograde direction, opposite the other planets, so the tilt is almost 180 degrees, it is considered to be spinning with its 'top', or north pole pointing 'downward' (southward). Uranus rotates almost on its side relative to the orbit, Pluto is pointing slightly 'down'. The ratios with Earth refer to the axis without reference to north or south.

**Mean Temperature**. This is the average temperature over the whole planet's surface (or for the gas giants at the one bar level) in degrees C (Celsius or Centigrade) or degrees F (Fahrenheit). For Mercury and the moon, for example, this is an average over the sunlit (very hot) and dark (very cold) hemispheres and so is not representative of any given region on the planet, and most of the surface is quite different from this average value. As with the earth, there will tend to be variations in temperature from the equator to the poles, from the day to night sides, and seasonal changes on most of the planets.

**Surface Pressure** (bars or atmospheres). This is the atmospheric pressure (the weight of the atmosphere per unit area) at the surface of the planet in bars or atmospheres.

The surfaces of Jupiter, Saturn, Uranus, and Neptune are deep in the atmosphere and the location and pressures are not known.

**Number of Moons**. This gives the number of IAU officially confirmed moons orbiting the planet. New moons are still being discovered.

**Ring System?** This tells whether a planet has a set of rings around it, Saturn being the most obvious example.

**Global Magnetic Field?** This tells whether the planet has a measurable large-scale magnetic field. Mars and the moon have localized regional magnetic fields but no global field.

# Resources from
# Creation Ministries International

## Creation magazine quarterly

This unique full-colour family magazine will keep you up-to-date on the latest evidence for biblical Creation and claims about evolution. Although written for laypeople, every effort is made to make sure the content is scientifically accurate. Children look forward to the beautifully illustrated full-colour children's section written specially for them, in every issue.

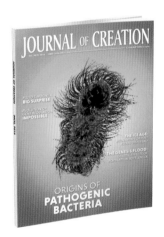

## Journal of Creation

Many believe that evolution is true because it is based upon a collection of scientific 'evidences'. But any scientist researching origins, whether it is evolution or even creation, is dealing with alleged historical events that we were not there to observe. As such, beliefs about origins play a pivotal role when interpreting facts (like rocks or fossils) or even data sets. Because most people only get to hear one side of the interpretation, our in-depth *Journal of Creation* sets out to make sense of our world from the standpoint of biblical origins.

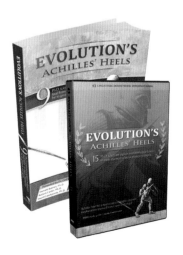

## Evolution's Achilles' Heels (Book & DVD)

*Nine Ph.D. scientists (book); 15 Ph.D. scientists (DVD)*

This book (available also as a DVD with subtitles in 16 languages) exposes the fatal flaws in the evolutionary beliefs associated with Natural Selection, Genetics and DNA, The Origin of Life, The Fossil Record, The Geological Record, Radiometric Dating, Cosmology, and Ethics and Morality. Each of the Ph.D. scientist authors is a specialist in his field.

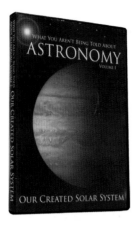

## Our Created Solar System DVD

*Presenter: Spike Psarris*

In this first DVD of the 3-vol. series: *What You Aren't Being Told About Astronomy* you will visit each of our solar system planets and many of their moons, through more than 230 breath-taking images from NASA and other sources. Each planet gives convincing scientific evidence that supports the Genesis account of creation, and refutes the evolutionary model. Many planets and moons appear to be young, not billions of years old; they also show evidence of design, not random processes.

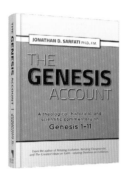

## The Genesis Account

*Dr Jonathan Sarfati*

This in-depth commentary on the crucial Genesis chapters 1–11 upholds the biblical creationist position of creation in six consecutive normal-length days about 6,000 years ago, death resulting from Adam's sin, a global Flood, and a confusion of languages at Babel. It shows how the rest of the Bible interprets Genesis in the above way, and answers the commonest objections to a plain understanding of this text.

## By Design

*Dr Jonathan Sarfati*

Case after case for amazing design in the living world, it demolishes theories of chemical evolution of the first life. Yet unlike many in the prominent Intelligent Design Movement, he is up-front about the truth of the Bible. This enables him to refute many anti-design arguments, and answer the key question: 'Who is the Designer?'

## Refuting Compromise

*Dr Jonathan Sarfati*

With his usual brilliant clarity, Jonathan Sarfati, author of the best-selling *Refuting Evolution* (Vols. 1 and 2) has produced a comprehensive and resounding refutation of the position of 'progressive creationist' Hugh Ross, whose views are causing massive confusion about science and the Bible. The most powerful theological and scientific defence of a straightforward view of Genesis creation ever written.

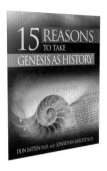

## 15 Reasons to Take Genesis as History
*Dr Don Batten and Dr Jonathan Sarfati*
This small book succinctly shows why those who believe in the inspiration of the Bible have no intellectually honest choice but to take Genesis as straightforward history, just as Jesus did. It powerfully challenges the idea that the Genesis account of creation is just some sort of ancient theological story and not actual history.

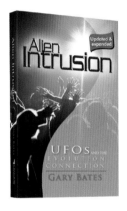

## Alien Intrusion: UFOs and the evolution connection (updated & expanded)
*Gary Bates*
In this landmark book (the only creation book ever to be an Amazon top 50 best-seller), Gary Bates unravels one of popular culture's enduring and growing phenomena. UFOs, crop circles, Roswell, alien abductions—it's all answered! The well researched data leads the reader inexorably to one conclusion: there is an 'intergalactic' battle over the history of life in the universe, and for the souls of human beings. Its eye-opening insights have already won souls for Christ. This new edition contains more pictures and a new chapter about alleged abductions based on extra research Gary has conducted.

## Days 1-7 - Your complete children's guide to the 7 days of Creation Week
*Russell Grigg*
A full-colour, glossy and beautifully illustrated guide to what God did on each day of Creation Week. It presents the truth about Creation in a way that will stimulate young minds and answer questions such as: Who made God? Is there life on Mars? Could the days have been millions of years? What about the big bang? Did God use evolution? A compilation of articles that have appeared in the Creation for Kids section of *Creation* magazine, it points children to Jesus Christ, the Creator and Saviour God.

## The True Story of the World
*Russell Grigg*
This is the true account of the seven most important events in the history of the world. Written for young minds and beautifully illustrated, it covers the creation of the world, the first sin, Noah's worldwide Flood, Babel, God's covenant, the death and resurrection of the Lord Jesus Christ, and the final consummation of all things when Christ returns.

# Creation Ministries
# International Offices

## Australia

PO Box 4545, Eight Mile Plains,
Qld 4113, Australia.
Phone: (07) 3340 9888
Fax: (07) 3340 9889
Email: aus@creation.info

## New Zealand

PO Box 39005, Howick,
Auckland, 2145, New Zealand.
Phone/Fax: (09) 537 4818
Email: nz@creation.info

## Singapore

Clementi Central PO Box 195,
Singapore 911207.
Republic of Singapore.
Email: singapore@creation.info

## South Africa

PO Box 3349,
Durbanville 7551, South Africa.
Phone: (021) 979 0107
Fax: (086) 519 0555
Email: sa@creation.info

## UK and Europe

15 Station Street, Whetstone,
Leicestershire, LE8 6JS
United Kingdom.
Phone: 0116 2848 999
Email: UK@creation.info

## Canada

300 Mill Street, Unit 7, Kitchener,
ON, N2M 5G8, Canada.
Phone: (519) 746 7616
Fax: (519) 746 7617
Subscriptions, books and videos
only: 1–888–251–5360
Email: canada@creation.info

## USA

PO Box 350, Powder Springs,
GA 30127, USA.
Phone: (800) 616-1264
Fax: (770) 439 9784
Email: US@creation.info

## Other Countries

Please contact Australian office.